JOURNAL
OF AN URBAN
ROBINSON CRUSOE

JOURNAL OF AN URBAN ROBINSON CRUSOE

LONDON AND BRIGHTON

Des Marshall

Saxon Books
SUSSEX UK

ISBN 0 9528969 3 1

First published 2002
By Saxon Books
London Road   Burgess Hill West Sussex RH15 9RN   UK

Phone 01 444 232 356

Web sites: www.warpoetry.co.uk and   www.saxonbooks.co.uk

First printing.
Printed and bound in Great Britain by Antony Rowe Ltd,
Eastbourne, UK.

We have applied to Penguin Books Ltd and Suhrkamp Verlag for
permission to use the extract from *Steppenwolf* by Hermann Hesse,
translated by Basil Crichton and revised by Walter Sorell. We have
been unable to trace Joy Cowley the author of *Vision* and would be
very pleased to hear from her.
Cover by Saxon Books and Michael White.

This book is dedicated to the following organisations and people: the staff and users of NDC; Jamestown Drop-In Centre, Adelaide Road London NW3; the Camden Mental Health Consortium, Hampstead Town Hall, London, NW3; and to Mr Fred Robinson, 1922-1992.

With acknowledgements and thanks to
Michael White (front cover illustration of main building and figure), Linda Rowel, Jan Shimmin, SarahWright.

Log Book

1994-2001

.

30 August 2001

Dear Reader,

I want to try and tell you the truth about this journal. I didn't write it. It was written by a man who called himself Urban Robinson Crusoe who, for some reason I don't understand, happened to look very much like me.

I met him late in 1994, December, I think it was. He didn't look very well. Small, nervous, thin faced. We met on a Mental Health Day Workshop in Camden. I remember he didn't say much, but seemed very aware of what was going on, nodding his head here and there.

We started to talk. After some ten minutes he asked if I would do him a favour. I said warily that it depended on what it was. He said he was writing a journal about his thoughts and feelings and could I try to get it published when it was finished. I suppose I thought him a bit of a nutter, but for some reason I said, "Sure," even though I didn't really believe him. He asked for my phone number, and noticing my hesitancy he assured me that he wouldn't ring or bother me until it was finished.

Earlier this month I received a phone call from him. Actually I had forgotten all about him after all these years. He wanted to see me again. Reluctantly I agreed to his request, not knowing what I was getting myself into.

We met in a cafe in Hampstead. He mentioned that he had always liked the area. Then he reached into a carrier bag, took out a folder full of papers and thrust it at me. It was the manuscript, and he was asking me if I would I try to get it published and pretend I had written it. I was flabbergasted.

I told him my objections to saying I had written it, but his pleadings and the look of utter despair on his face got to me so I said I would, just to calm him down. He seemed to relax after that, bought me another cup of coffee, rolled a cigarette and smoked it, made some small talk, and to my amazement suddenly got up and left, not giving me an address or contact number.

And I haven't seen him since.

Des Marshall

1994
Camden, London

23 November

I am Urban Robinson Crusoe. I exist on an Island of Urban confusion, with no Girl Friday. I keep my head when all around are losing theirs and blaming it on each other. I live my separate reality. I am an independent witness to the chaos and disintegration that abounds around me.

The roar of the traffic outside my fifth floor flat suddenly demands attention from my tired mind.

I force my attention onto this piece of blank paper. A scream from the playground in the centre of this rundown estate startles me out of the sequence of words that were slipping through the cortex of my brain. Another scream and bellow with a high pitched cry start to unnerve me. I am aware of the pressure of the small, blue, betting shop biro on the paper. My fingers start to go numb with pins and needles running down from the wrist that was broken six months ago.

For a few moments peace descends. Suddenly the hum of the fridge breaks the uneasy silence. The shouts and screams of the playground start again and play with my concentration. I lift my aching neck and stare at the grimy stains on the yellowing dirty lino on the kitchen floor. Small pockets of dirt, like on a hairy man's back, filter through my eyes to my awareness and I feel guilty that I am unable to gather energy to clean the greasy stains on the gas cooker which seems to stand there so majestically.

I feel lost in linear time. The clock seems to have stopped. I go over to see. It is still ticking: 2.15 p.m. I think I have been indoors for hours, but it has only been thirty-five minutes. It seems so long, so long. My memories present me with pictures that take me back to long forgotten times when I couldn't breathe because a force was squeezing the life out of me as if it didn't want me to live, wanting to terminate the existence of this child. I learned later that this experience was called Asthma. And I see a small child kneeling in prayer, asking God to let him go home from the Institution.

25 November

My physical body perturbs me. I look in the mirror a lot more than usual lately. It's not out of vanity, more out of a concern. My mental image of myself resembles nothing like reality. The truth is a sort of shock at my own existence. I notice my receding hairline and greying hair. My physical attractiveness is now becoming less of a concern to me - as physical contact becomes a problem. I recoil from bodily touch. I am an outsider looking in. I have never belonged to any particular group of people, but mixed with all kinds. I feel they are parts of my personality, although my alienation makes it impossible to be really linked with them, even though they are human parts of me.

The outsiders are the only people to see the futility of existence going on around them, not the Nine-to-Fivers, the robots, the urban and suburban Mr Joneses, who probably make love to their wives like involuntary robots, twice a week, never on Sundays. The heretics were the true leaders of life. They walked on the edge of society, the independent thinkers, free from the slow, deadly disintegration of mediocre existence.

27 November

Holloway. "Oh, he's hip," I heard the black shoe salesman say to the two young girl assistants in the shoe shop. The man was trying to impress the girls with his knowledge of "street cred," as they say, being streetwise. They were talking about some guy they knew. I felt contempt for the young man as I had a feeling he had tried to take the mickey out of me when I walked into the shop. I knew I looked rough. The cold always affected me, making my nose glow red and making me have to constantly wipe it. Hip? What's bloody hip? I felt uneasy trying on the shoes, feeling the girls' eyes watching me. I had on a red and white bobble hat that my alcoholic brother had given me, who in turn had got it from one of the handout centres he frequents regularly. It looked like a small tea cosy, the kind that women used to put over teapots years ago to keep the tea warm. It keeps me warm too. That's all I care.

I felt I had better concentrate on getting some shoes because my paranoid unease had started to bubble up. I crossed to the other side of the shop to try on some other shoes that were on the stand. I could not make up my mind. I have become very indecisive lately, too much going on inside. I still felt one of the girls watching me. I wondered if she reckoned I looked "hip." I had to laugh to myself at the thought. I felt quite happy about not looking hip, after many years of putting on an act - an image that wasn't me.

The shop had started to fill up and the two girls had wandered off, serving customers. I finally made a decision and approached the girl near the till. She smiled in a half-hearted manner. I wondered if it was an acquired shop smile or a smirk, knowing I was not hip.

I went out into the street, aware that my alienation would envelop me like a protective cloud. I felt numb inside. Each step was an effort as my feet touched the sloping uneven ground of the paving stones. The streets were cold and grey. I looked at the faces of people. Some looked like they were in hell, with their haggard, grief-stricken faces and vacant eyes as they wandered the dirty litter-filled streets.

The streets made me feel uneasy. Some people seemed to stare. I had to avoid staring back. The streets were filled with tension, and aggression wasn't very far away. One man who happened to stare too long got a mouthful as he walked by, but he just went on walking without turning round.

The streets were important to me. I needed them to get rid of pent-up feelings inside. My long walks would relax me enough so I could sleep at night. The nights were times of remembering, but I am not sure the memories belonged to me, like the times when I used to wait at the Institution gates of the Home I was in, waiting for my mother to visit me, waiting, waiting, waiting through the long drawn out space of endless time. And now my life seems to be one long wait. For what? Somewhere I knew I had the answer, but dared not rake through too deeply the turbid depth of my knowing.

29 November

It's afternoon and I am in Euston Station Cafeteria musing on the topic of if I did right spending £12.50 on acupuncture. The middle-aged Chinese lady doctor didn't seem to understand me. And I had difficulty understanding her because her English sounded more Chinese than English to me. Anyway, if it helps to stop the pins and needles in my fingers . . .

I did right by having a large tea, paying only 5p extra.

Unable to go home yet, feeling cut off. My flat seems like a prison waiting to be occupied.

I become aware of the serviette I used to mop up the spilt tea. It's blood red. Suddenly, the woman opposite me attracts my attention. She has blood red lipstick and blood red finger nails. I feel invisible among this anxious, hurried energy that railway stations create. There are five women opposite me. Their northern accent wafts over me as I gather my thoughts to write. I'm sitting in the smoking section of the cafeteria. I giggle as I notice clouds of smoke billowing around us puffing billies. We look at each other with quick sidelong glances that create a sort of indifferent curiosity among us.

The lady with the blood red lipstick suddenly looks at me. I wonder if she has guessed that I might be writing about her. I feel slightly guilty about it. Pins and needles in my hand stop me writing. A large group of people sit down near me, ignoring me. They are irritated by the high prices, so they are eating their own food, justifying themselves: well, we bought tea in the cafeteria. I become aware that they're all around me, talking across me. Startled by what's happening I get nervous and begin gathering my bits of writing up, growing very self-conscious, intensely aware of every move I make. They start to laugh. I feel their eyes on me as I walk away. Suddenly I have become very, very visible. I once read somewhere that hell is other people. I walk to my prison.

1 December

When I broke my wrist, the evening after it had been reset by the hospital two friends came to see me. Strangely, they weren't English: Stefan, a Russian dissident, who in the eighties was tortured by the KGB, and Ivo, a German healer who set up a spiritual healing section in an alternative medicine centre in Old Street. There seems something surreal about this event, as I have lived all my life in England and Ivo's father was in the Hitler Youth and fought in the Second World War against England. My grandfather came from Russia and my father fought against Hitler's Germany. Stefan's father also fought against the Third Reich on the Russian front. The cold war separated England from Russia, but we became friends with Germany, so our parents at one time or another in history were against each other. Now their offspring are friends.

I've been thinking about self-esteem. Why is it so important to have and why do some people have it and others don't, and if they have it, why do they, or why should they - and if they don't have it, why don't they, or why shouldn't they. These questions matter to me because it's a feeling, according to psychologists, that's important to have if you are going to have a quality of life.

For a great many people, if they don't have a job their self-esteem goes down, but if they get a job, sometimes just a menial job, it goes up. Their whole life changes. This feeling is very illusory because some people are working and still have low self-esteem. The psychologically healthiest people apparently are people who are involved in a cause outside of themselves. Maybe they are saying we should all be helping each other more, and that possibly then our society would have less problems than it does have. Instinctively, to me, it sounds right but then who am I? Just an Urban Robinson Crusoe, with not enough self-esteem to talk about it.

2 December

Thoughts: Jeffrey Darma, the serial killer in America, was pronounced, sane. How can this be? The man killed about sixteen men and had bits of them all over the house, in pots, in his pockets. Apparently he did this because he was lonely and wanted them near him. If that's normal then judging morality on a scale, I would be classed a saint because I don't do things like that.

I'm feeling closed in. I need nature. It's 5.30 a.m. and I can't sleep any more. I was thinking of walking to Regents Park along the canal but the weather is very changeable. It's December and there is going to be hail and heavy downpours. Why I am undecided about it is that people zoom down the path on their bikes. They don't seem to care about people walking. A week before I broke my arm I heard a bell tinkle. I looked behind me and couldn't believe what I saw - a man on a bike with two huge Doberman pinschers running alongside him, bearing down on me, racing along like a man possessed. Now

I'm sure he was insane and maybe Jeffrey Darma was normal after all, because I doubt if he would do that.

4 December

I find women very attractive lately. I wonder why I never really noticed before. Attraction, now there's a thing, and sex. I watched a programme on TV, I think it was *Kilroy*. They have an invited audience to discuss certain subjects affecting society. This programme was about legalising prostitution. Kilroy asked, "Isn't it dangerous?" A lot of the, shall we say, professional ladies agreed and sometimes, especially when one of their friends is murdered, they get really frightened. One lady said she had been raped, kidnapped and gang-banged, beaten up, thrown out of a window. Then she said, unbelievably, she enjoyed her work. I'm sure she was on drugs because of the way she spoke, with a slur.

In a way, I hope she was, because it comes back to what a psychologist might say: she is absolutely sane. To say she enjoyed her work after all those terrible things had happened to her makes you think maybe Jeffrey Darma was sane after all. At least he did terrible things to other people. There is a sort of perverse logic in that.

7 December

I want to tell you a story, as Max Bygraves would say. I was walking over Primrose Hill feeling really low and ugly, not aware of people properly, even avoiding them, when a beautiful little girl unexpectedly came up to me and said, "Please, sir, would you be my Valentine?" giving me daisy and buttercup flowers. I said something like, "Oh yes, thank you," and as I walked away I saw her mother give me a brief smile. I had to walk quickly away because I was so overcome I thought I would break down in tears. I'm sure she must have been an angel, because it was exactly what I needed to break the black mood I was in. I didn't even know it was St Valentine's Day until later.

Afterwards, I started to think maybe her mother saw how low I looked and told her to do it. It made me remember a story that a friend who was studying psychology told me. He was studying a case history of a man who felt so alienated from people and society that he was on his way to commit suicide when a woman said "Good morning" to him. It actually stopped him doing the act. It somehow broke the mould. At the time he told me I didn't believe him that somehow somebody saying "Good morning" would stop one killing oneself. After the event on Primrose Hill I can understand it.

It reminds me of the words to a Neil Young song, *My Heart Needs Relating not Solitude*. Loneliness, I think, is the disease of the nineties, which probably began in Thatcher's eighties.

I wonder if people notice in London that the width of the main roads is getting smaller, about ten feet smaller, with cars parked all along the roads opposite each other, each car I suppose being about five feet wide.

10 December

I feel depressed. I left my scarf in Euston Station yesterday while having a cup of coffee with my Russian friend, Stefan. I can't understand how I forgot it because when we left it was quite cold and raining. I started to blame Stefan because he was in a very tense mood and when he is in this mood he can become exhausting and I didn't notice because I was distracted by his mood. But I had to remind myself that I have lost things before without Stefan being around. Even so, I still feel uptight with him. And why should I be so depressed about losing a scarf with all the terrible things going on around the world or even in this country, or even in this block of flats, which I know do go on because I hear the screams and shouts of abuse and sometimes see syringes laying about! But it was such a good scarf, a scarf I really liked.

I went back to Euston Station to see if somebody had handed it in. I spoke to the table clearer who I recognised from yesterday. I got the impression when he went into the staff office that he knew about it but he came out empty handed and said a customer had taken it. I said, "How can a customer take it when it was in the staff office? You mean a staff member has taken it."

He said, "No, a customer."

I said, "But it wasn't his scarf."

He said, "It had been there for a long time." On his badge was written *Customer Care*. He certainly was looking after his customers - giving them scarves that didn't belong to them. He clarified it was in the exact position I was sitting in. The trouble was he wasn't English. I think he was from India, and he didn't speak very good English.

I said, "It must have been staff because how would a customer know there was a scarf in the staff room?"

He said, "No, a customer."

I had to walk away because I was just repeating myself. I was getting more and more frustrated. He was starting to talk faster and faster with his hands flapping, becoming hysterical.

11 December

Here comes a feeling of melancholia or sadness, a sort of indifference to my surroundings. I feel like Sidney Carlton in *A Tale of Two Cities*. Nothing's of any value. Geoffrey's dad's idea seems appropriate, "Nothing really matters." But I have noticed, when we say something, sometime later the opposite applies, and some things do matter - like my feelings, which were hurt the other day when when I asked a woman something and she replied very abruptly, "Oh, don't bother me! Oh ... Er ... Erm ... Go over to her over there and talk to her about it." She had pushed in while I was talking to somebody and at the same time she was stuffing a sandwich in her mouth, like a praying mantis swaying from side to side trying to hypnotise its victim. It was her tone of voice that upset me, sort of dismissing me. I was so angry I walked away, waiting for her to stop talking so I could talk to her about it. When she stopped I went up to her and pointed out what I felt about it. She made a grimace and apologised in a way.

Another chap came up and heard some of the conversation. I had previously spoken to him about self-esteem - and I can imagine what he said, "Oh, he's got low self-esteem." The thing that worried me more was that I couldn't let it go. I was so angry. I felt I was too soft on her and I felt I wanted revenge. I was so hurt. Where did all this rage come from? I could have murdered her but I also realised if I had done so this feeling still would have remained. It disabled me all day and I wonder in society what happens when people are unable to control their hurts and they lash out at people, not possibly out of cruelty but because they feel hurt and put-down when some long forgotten memory reawakens, when somebody says something or acts in a certain way.

It seems understandable if all these hurts are in human beings that whole nations go to war over them. Possibly, sometime in history their people were attacked, raped, tortured etc. and each soldier has his own hurt to take out on others. In the First World War they went in their hundreds of thousands to enlist to happily kill the so-called Bosch, probably not even knowing why they were doing it, taking their own rage to war.

12 December

It's 5 a.m. I can't sleep any more. I had a good rest yesterday and didn't go out at all. It rained all day and London can get exhausting if you're out too long, especially this area, Camden Town. Everywhere you walk there are people, I mean, crowds of people. You are either walking around them, bumping into them, trying to get out their way, dodging traffic, avoiding beggars because you feel guilty about them. It's okay if you have some loose change in your hand, you can drop it in their hand, but when you stop to look in your pocket and bring out maybe pound coins all this seems to take a long time. You don't want to give a pound coin and when they start to look longingly at them you start to feel uneasy and want to get away. That's why I think a lot of people don't give.

Around this area beggars seem to be sitting down on the pavement in a passive position. Maybe to get sympathy or perhaps begging becomes exhausting with all those people walking past you, ignoring your pleas. A lot of them must feel completely abandoned and rejected. Apparently, reading about people who have been on the streets, they feel better if you talk to them or have a kind word to say.

I suppose that's not much to ask - or is it, these days?

I am on my knees writing this, no, not praying. My back and neck are so painful. I am sure it's to do with tension over the years, and kneeling is the only way I can feel comfortable.

It's 6.30 a.m. I have been writing for an hour and a half. Another statement from psychologists is that people who get up very early are I depressed - is that last "I" I wrote a Freudian slip? This psychology can drive one to start to have one's head examined.

13 December

I'm coming back to the subject of self-esteem again - the spiritual world or higher consciousness, or God, whatever you want to call this other state of being that is based on love and is altruistic. Self-esteem doesn't exist because there is no judgment of you or your value to society - either by you or others. You are just a being of light that exists to learn about its light and, like Tinkerbell in Peter Pan. If people or yourself don't believe in your light, i.e., self-esteem, your light starts to go out. Because of this Tinkerbell started to die, and it's only your own self-belief that's going to bring it back to life - when you start to believe it.

Strangely enough, if you believe in your own light and worth other people see it, believe it, and it starts to exist. Because the children started to believe in Tinkerbell her light became brighter. She grew stronger and started to live again. As the mystics say, we can create our own reality.

What does it avail me if I create writing good enough to be published, or if I am able to prophesy or gain knowledge, or have power over other people, or multiply wealth, if I have not love? All these are as useless as a stupid ripple in a bloody ocean. Corinthians 1, Chapter 13.

I saw a tramp this morning. I have seen him before walking around Camden Town. To me, he seems very destitute - long, matted hair down his back, no socks, shoes over on their side, worn down, dirty, unkempt clothes. He seems to be walking more slowly than ever. He has an alsatian dog with him all the time.

The dog seemed to be very concerned about him because he kept looking up at him every few seconds.

Suddenly, I was quite taken aback because it dawned on me that this dog loved this human being, when probably nobody else did, and I suppose human beings have to get love somewhere, if they can't get it from other humans they get it from animals. If they can't get it from either, for their own personal reasons they turn to God, or television, or drink, or whatever.

19 December

I feel awful, like the bottom's fallen out of me. No energy, dragging my body around like it's a ton weight.

I am trying to work out why I am like this. Is it Camden Town, always so depressing, and crowded and exhausting? (Why do I get a feeling of deja vu? I take away the traffic in my mind and I'm back to Charles Dickens' time, when he lived here, with the beggars, the dirt, the sordidness and drunkenness).

Or is it the weather? It's so schizophrenic! Changeable: sunny, rain, cold, a greyish colour covering everything.

Or is it the negative news I can't escape from? If I put *Classic FM* or *Melody Radio* on they still churn it out every half hour. I once asked *Melody Radio* if it was some law that if you are granted a franchise to broadcast you must give the news every half-hour. The response was, "No, I don't think so." She couldn't comment any further as she was just the telephone operator.

I suddenly thought she probably was the cleaner, just passing, and picked up the phone because it was ringing. It was quite late at night when she answered.

Or is it being alone for so long that's so exhausting? I wonder if Robinson Crusoe, if he existed, felt this. I read once that there was a real life Robinson Crusoe who lived on an island somewhere. Oh, I can't write any more, this is bloody ridiculous, I feel so weak and apathetic.

20 December

I still feel uptight about *Melody Radio*'s indifference to my complaint yesterday about negative news, so I have written to the BBC Complaints Department.

BBC
Complaints Department
Broadcasting House
London   SW1A 1AA

Dear Sir or Madam

I have a question to ask and it has been on my mind for sometime. Is it a prerequisite of the broadcasting license that radio stations must give frequent updates of the news if they are to be allowed to broadcast?

I don't know of any radio station that doesn't give the news - from *Melody Radio, Classic FM,. Jazz FM, Capital Radio, News Direct Radio,* to *Talk Back Radio,* and all other independent radio stations. The BBC radio programmes, with all the rest, churn out this worrying news day in, day out, 99% of which is negative news. We cannot escape from it.

As an avid radio listener mainly BBC programmes I might add, I am undermined by it. I can't escape from this news. I try and run to switch it off, but it's generally too late.

Is it any wonder that there is so much depression and anger around, when this stuff is fed into your subconscious daily? Instant trauma right into your front room from anywhere in the world - as if there aren't terrible things going on locally or worrisome things in one's own life.

It's not as if there was lack of access to news. We have TV news, Sky TV news, broadsheet news, tabloids news, magazine news, local paper news, and even local libraries have the news. This amounts to an unwarranted and unsparing attack on our senses.

Surely there could be one radio station that doesn't give the news so that people can have peace and enjoy the programmes, preferably *Radio 3* or *Radio 4* or *Classic FM.* By making these news-free radio programmes you would be helping people, and not undermining them.

Come on, be ahead of your time. Become an EMOTIONALLY as well as an environmentally friendly broadcaster. Give us peace. It's well known that stress is the biggest problem in society today. Tell people to switch to another programme if they want the news. Send a questionnaire to listeners asking if they would like a news free station. I know what the answer would be.

Yours faithfully,

U.R. Crusoe.

22 December

Some days I intentionally don't wash. The reason is it gives me a sense of freedom from boring ritual and mechanical existence, which I think is the cause sometimes of exhaustion. We need to do different things and use our imagination to stop this passivity which I feel can lead to depression.

I sometimes wonder if the "universal mind" really exists, because something happened to me that makes me think maybe it does. I was walking to Camden Town one day and I saw one of my mother's old friends. We always talk and I sometimes go to see her in her flat. On seeing her coming towards me I felt so glad to see her. I wanted to put my arms around her.

What happened was, when we met we both put our arms around each other. This has never happened before and I have known Ann since I was a child. I think she was a little embarrassed. I wasn't, funnily enough.

1995
Camden, London

4 January

I have left out the rest of December. It was horrendous, including Christmas, which I spent alone, like Robinson Crusoe. I think I am a broken man, a sick man. That's why I live this precarious life, a life cut off from intimacy. Because of a feeling of inadequacy I don't have the capacity or the grounding to be involved with another. Sometimes I think this is self-indulgent, and pessimistic. Even though I think this, I don't challenge this pessimistic outlook with positive action, because of a dread that it might be true that I am a defective flawed human being. I sort of checkmate myself, caught in my own web of terror. I don't think I am alone in this. I think there are millions of Robinson Crusoes out there.

I read a book called *Beyond Cinderella*. It's about how women can find a partner. I was fascinated by it. She tells how to research the problem, like you would go out to search methodically for a job. But you must be prepared for rejection, and rejection, that's the way she put it, if you want to find your prince or princess. She does workshops for men as well as women. It's called "Connecting." I don't know why I am writing about all this. I am just an observer in these areas and the idea of being rejected, and rejected, brings forth feelings of bleeding wounds. I'm toppling on the edge and that might open up the abyss below me.

16 January

My God, I feel so frustrated, so mixed up, so alienated. I can't figure out where to go today. I have left my flat. I felt okay at home, reading, typing, pottering about. I don't know why I even came out. I felt I had better do so because I had not left my flat at all yesterday.

I had fish and chips that I didn't really want. I left half the chips. It cost me £3.70, which I couldn't really afford. I went to the library in Hampstead Heath. I couldn't concentrate on reading so I walked around Keats' House, not knowing if I was feeling interested.

I sat in the garden and played my Dictaphone tape back. I had done a recording with Peter, a friend of mine, when we were at the Royal Festival Hall together.

We had been discussing Albert Camus.

Then I went into a betting shop and lost a pound. I started to get anxious and panicky and had to go to the toilet. I felt nervous when I looked at people, so I avoided looking at them and instead I stared into space.

I have grown my beard again. It makes me feel better as it hides the emotional turmoil that shows on my face. Suddenly my consciousness slips down to first gear and I feel exhausted and have to drag my body home to my flat.

25 January

I have a watch that keeps stopping. It needs these small batteries that are supposed to last for eighteen months. Mine keeps stopping after six months. It stopped last week so I decided to buy another watch. I could not decide what type, the winder or battery. This indecision went on for over a week. Being very undecided, I didn't really want to buy a new one.

On TV last night there was a programme called *Beyond Belief*. Uri Geller was on. He is a magician and, I suppose, an illusionist. And probably a good psychologist. He told people to get out all their watches that don't work. I got out my watch. He told people to hold their watches in one hand and after he had counted to three, to shout out "Go!"

He had a practice run and then had the camera looking into his eyes. He counted "1, 2, 3" and "Go!" and lo and behold my watch started to go. I really hadn't expected it to.

Sadly, it stopped after three hours.

The next day I tried to do it myself, doing ALL the things correctly, like he said. It wouldn't work. Maybe he does have some power. People's watches started going after five years, ten years. They had been asked to bring their watches to the studio.

Viewers were phoning in saying their watches were going and their keys were bending. One man who phoned in said he was supposed to go out in half an hour and the key to his car was bent. Also, a grandfather clock that had belonged to his father and grandfather, which had never tick-tocked, had started to tick – amazing stuff.

3 February

It's 3.30 a.m. and I can't sleep. I woke up feeling terrible, sort of nauseous. It's not what I ate. It's to do with anxiety and alienation.

It feels like being suspended in a void, unable to cling to anything, like my mind is going to give way, to seize up or disintegrate. I suppose insanity begins like this, the only thing that helps is to concentrate my thoughts on writing to occupy my mind, to fill it up with something.

11 February

Something has happened that might change my outlook on life, or my perceptions about where I belong. I am moving to

Brighton. Surprise, surprise. It happened so quickly.

I applied to Brighton Council for a home of some sort, last year about this time, February, and after about three months they offered me a bedsit. I turned it down. I wanted something equivalent, at least, to what I have got, a one bedroom flat.

I heard no more until January this year. They passed my details on to a housing association and after a few weeks they offered me this flat. I had to make a quick decision after seeing it. I accepted. Now I am moving this Thursday to Brighton.

It's in a place called Whitehawk, about one and a half miles from the centre of Brighton. Not quite the Urban Robinson Crusoe anymore.

What do I do now?

Brighton

15 February

I suppose I am a Brightonian now. I still wander the streets but it's just so much more pleasant to do that here, and I see many so-called Robinson Crusoes, who don't realise what they have become.

Brighton is a strange town of contrasting types of people jumbled up and thrown together: the very poor, the very rich, gangsters, day-trippers, the unemployed coming down for the summer from the cities, possibly to get work for the season, students from other countries to learn English, artists, writers, street performers. Well-off showbiz people live here, and there's a big gay scene.

Graham Greene, the writer, who lived in Brighton, called Brighton a fugitive town. There is a sort of truth in that; people are always coming and going, just like London.

There are mad people thrown out of the asylums that they

are closing down. There is a big one at Haywards Heath, half way between London and Brighton. The inmates have a choice when they leave, London or Brighton. Most opt for Brighton, for reasons I would think are obvious. Anything you want in London you can get here.

27 February

Well here I am at my desk, wondering what to say about being, I suppose, a sort of seaside town Urban Robinson Crusoe. After moving, I can understand people not bothering to move or even, for that matter, to take up residence. To have no fixed abode instead, because the stress is quite considerable. Changing the gas, the electricity, the water rates, if you don't read the meters correctly or on time you can be responsible for a hefty bill that's nothing to do with you.

If you are on income support and claim housing benefit it's amazing what can go wrong - either the clerks don't hear you properly or they are so stressed themselves in as much as they are overworked and there are so many claimants because of the unemployment situation or the system is so complicated and changing so much that they don't understand it themselves.

I was able to go to a creative writing workshop in Brighton last week, which was quite interesting, especially in realising - oh, I will have to finish what I was going to say later, talking about things going wrong, or things not happening.

10 March

I feel so bloody frustrated! That's what I have felt in Brighton, since moving. I don't know if other people experience what I feel, they probably do, but it feels like it only happens to me.

I have been waiting for a washing machine to be delivered this morning and they never turned up. I waited till one o'clock, getting more and more angry. About ten past one my instinct was telling me this could happen. It was a lovely, sunny morning and I wanted to go out; that's why I was so frustrated.

I had decided to get a washing machine because it was just as expensive to go to the washerette, which cost about £3.50 per week. It's about the same price as a washing machine, with no interest on top. You don't have the hassle of walking to the washerette and back and maybe waiting for a machine.

24 March

It's 2.30 a.m. and I can't sleep any more. I went to bed early, about 9 p.m. I felt so tired. Since I've been up I have had all sorts of feelings going through me. There was a talk on the radio about mid-life crisis in men, also a lot of news about a bomb going off in Oklahoma City, outside a Federal building, killing possibly hundreds of people. I feel very angry about this, and sad, and also pessimistic about the way our world is going. The different ideologies that certain factions have, justifying their dogma with acts of violence. There again, we can't be sure, it could well be a certain individual with a grudge against somebody in the Federal building or, for that matter, the FBI.

I'm finding it very hard to write since being in Brighton. I am feeling apathetic about things. Bloody hell, I am still here, still sort of living. So what do I do now? Is it the mid-life crisis that the people were talking about on the radio? And a very enlightening discussion it was. The people talking had a great insight into the problem, if you can call it that. There were, I think, four men and two women and the presenter, who happened to be a man. He was very witty and kept the discussion flowing. One of the speakers said a man could feel he is in a mid-life crisis if, at forty-five years old, he is concerned because he hasn't written his novel or done any serious writing. I had a feeling, does he know me, something like that. "Strange?"

9 April

I have a lot of trouble with the concept of "sod's law." It seems to keep happening to me. I went to the supermarket yesterday, I got to the checkout, stood in the queue, the one with the least people in it standing with their shopping, waiting there. I suddenly realised the next queue was much smaller, so I went into that queue, feeling chuffed that I was next to be checked out.

The person who had been in front of me in the queue I had just left was now a couple of people behind. I felt very pleased with myself and was congratulating myself on my ingenuity, when suddenly there was a problem with the woman in front of me. She had spilt some milk over the checkout desk and they had to get assistance in case it affected the bar code, also to get another carton of milk and clean up the desk. I watched the other queue that I was originally in shrink and even the people that were behind me in that queue were being checked out and walking out. I had to watch in dismay as my bus pulled out of the precinct outside and which I could easily have caught if I had stayed in the original queue instead. I watched helplessly while this shambles was going on in front of me. There wasn't another bus for half an hour.

"Why me?" I spoke to the woman on the till about it and also the customer concerned. They seemed to think it only happens to them. It seems a lot of people are afflicted with this sod's law problem but I'm sure it only happens to me.

15 April

After three months I still have had no reply to my letter of complaint to the BBC, so what's the point of the BBC having a complaints department?

17 April

I am going to say something which I can't really believe myself. I think I miss LONDON, but trying to reveal what I miss about London and what irritates me about Brighton I am finding very difficult to put into words, or explain.

21 April

I have felt very stressed out these last three weeks. I thought I was on the verge of a nervous breakdown, trying to adjust to this strange town, where anything goes, and a sort of undercurrent of instability reigns. Everybody seems to be wanting to do their own thing.

I believe that Brighton has more disturbed people in relation to the size of the population, than any other town in the country. There's a sort of unreality about the town. It's too frivolous. People don't really listen to each other. They seem very excited and distracted. Is it because it's a holiday town, with too many distractions - the sea, the beach, the pier, the pretty women (there seems so many of them here), the men on the prowl for women, the buskers, the beach cafés with their coloured sunshades and ice-cream adverts, a sense of permanent holidaying atmosphere. It distracts people, even if you live here. You get sort of sucked into the excitement and get distracted.

In London you have to be focused to get things done. In London, because it's so huge, you can have some anonymity. In Brighton you're noticed. You can't really hide. I suppose in a way, you get slotted as a certain type of person by what you wear or how you look.

People wear such odd clothes that don't really match. Could be, sort of punk, with a bit of hippy thrown in, or mohair with greatcoat, or a collar and tie man, with shorts of different colours, possibly even with a bowler hat.

By the way, my washing machine was leaking again and flooded the woman's kitchen below. That's what nearly tipped me over the edge. This is the second time in two weeks this has happened. The engineer that fixed the first leak, I said to him,

"Suppose it happens again?"

He said, "It won't happen."

In fact I asked him twice. He said it very arrogantly, "It won't happen." He was the same engineer who came again yesterday to fix the leak again.

I wanted to get out of the contract so I could just use the washerette down the road and if you think I am imagining this idea of sod's law, walking past the washerette yesterday, I noticed that it had a notice in the window that said, *Sorry, Closed,* and all the washing machines had gone. Only the bare concrete floor was left.

29 April

This evening I had a prescription for a device that's supposed to fit over my asthma inhaler to help the steroid to get into my lungs. It didn't fit my inhaler so the device is useless. Evidently, this device is used all over the country to help asthma sufferers with steroid inhalers and apparently the number of asthma sufferers is soaring. What is happening? The mind boggles.

I am beginning to have negative feelings about this place called Brighton. I am becoming disturbed, angry and depressed. I have a feeling I would like to go into myself and not come out and say goodbye to the world. It sounds very attractive. I suppose many people do and don't come out. They go mad, and have to be committed. People might pity them but it might be their choice. I am not blaming anybody else for my own inadequacy and hopelessness.

Is it PARANOIA? I would call Brighton *Paranoia City.*

A friend of mine, Dr Peter Chadwick, sent me his new book that's just come out called *Understanding Paranoia.* That's what made me come to this conclusion about Brighton. It's also made me aware of my own paranoia, at times in Brighton. Like the other day, I was approaching a bus stop and was looking behind me to see if a bus was due, when a man said to me, "Is one due?" and I thought he was saying, in a double meaning context, "Is this a Jew?" referring to me. As it so happens, I am half Jewish. A bus "due" could sound like "Jew." MY mind, when I had left my flat, was preoccupied with concern about how I look, and the fact that I look quite Jewish.

3 May

Today, I feel emotionally dead, no passion or interest in anything, no energy, no point, only the ghosts of past friends to haunt me. I sit in my armchair for hours, sometimes doing nothing. Just thinking and watching my mind flowing, with images, like my own video projector and, like Michael Jackson, it's my own personal HIStory.

15 May

In Brighton, a superficiality and frivolity hides an undercurrent of despair and chaos, which I don't want to be a part of. This reminds me of a passage from. Herman Hesse, a book entitled *Steppenwolf* and written seventy years ago.

> My regret was for the present day, and for all the countless hours and days that I lost in mere passivity that brought me nothing, not even the shocks of awakening.
>
> But, thank God, there were exceptions. There were now and then, though rarely, the hours that brought the welcome shock, pulled down the walls and brought me back again from my wanderings to the living heart of the world.
>
> Sadly, and yet deeply moved, I set myself to recall the last of these experiences. It was at a concert of lovely, old music. After two or three notes of the piano the door was opened all of a sudden to the other world. I sped through Heaven and saw God at work. I suffered holy pains. I dropped all my defences and was afraid of nothing in the

world. I accepted all things and to all things I gave up my heart. It did not last very long, a quarter of an hour perhaps; but it returned to me in a dream at night and since, through all the barren days, I caught a glimpse of it now and then. Sometimes, for a minute or two, I saw it clearly, threading my life like a divine golden track.

But nearly always it was blurred in dirt and dust. Then again, it gleamed out in golden sparks as though never to be lost again and yet was soon quite lost once more. Once it happened as I lay awake at night, that I suddenly spoke in verses, in verses so beautiful and strange that I did not venture to think of writing them down and in the morning they vanished and yet they lay hidden within me like the hard kernel of an old brittle husk.

Once it came to me while reading a poet, while pondering a thought of Descartes, of Pascal; again, it shone out and drove its gold track far into the sky while I was in the presence of my beloved. Ah, it is hard to find this track of the divine in the midst of this life we lead, in this besotted humdrum age of spiritual blindness, with its architecture, its business, its politics, its men! How could I fail to be a lone wolf, an uncouth hermit, as I did not share one of its aims nor understand one of its pleasures? I cannot remain for long in either theatre or movie. I can scarcely read a paper, seldom a modern book. I cannot understand what pleasures and joys they are that drive people to the over-crowded railways and hotels, in the packed cafés with the suffocating and obtrusive music, to the bars and variety entertainments, to World Exhibitions, to the Corsos. I cannot understand nor share these joys, though they are within my reach, for which thousands of others strive. On the other hand, what happens to me in my rare hours of joy, what for me is bliss and life and ecstasy and exalta-tion, the world in general seeks at most in works of fiction; in life it finds absurd. And, in fact, if the world is right, if this music of the cafés, these mass enjoyments and these

Americanised men who are pleased with so little, are right, then I am wrong. I am crazy. I am in truth the Steppenwolf that I often call myself; that beast astray who finds neither home nor joy nor nourishment in a world that is strange and incomprehensible to him.

And indeed, I am the Urban Robinson Crusoe, who walks the streets of Brighton, like the invisible man, avoiding the cafés, discos, the beach bars with the bang, bang, bang, of rap music blaring out, the day trippers and holiday makers' exuberance and sense of complete letting go in a complete distraction from their worries, or, for that matter, the residents of Brighton, who get caught up in the escapism of superficiality.

21 May

Contradictorily, I let myself get caught up in this superficiality now and again. I am unable to do it for very long, a couple of hours probably, then reality returns.

Apparently depressives are more in touch with reality than ordinary people, according to psychologists who have done tests with people, so I could be called a realist or a depressive. They are both supposed to be negative so I suppose I might as well live in a fantasy world and pretend everything is okay and wonderful.

Apparently, from what I can gather from all this, if you think positively, i.e. pretend, you might draw positive things to you. Could that also include love, position, affluence, etc? Sounds very "new age" to me. The "In a world of broken dreams strive to be happy," quote comes to my mind.

26 May

Some people are so damaged that any innocent thing you say can be twisted and turned and they can react in a startling manner. Example: a friend of mine, Ruby (that is her real name, just in case she reads this because it might help her?), she was decorating my kitchen. She loves decorating. She asked me if I had a scrubbing brush. I said, "Yes, I showed you one yesterday, when I brought it out of the drawer."

She said, "No, you didn't."

I said, "Yes, I'm sure you remember."

"No, you didn't!" she said, getting angry.

I walked into the front room to get out of the way, knowing that this was getting out of hand.

She came and followed me, saying, "No, you didn't!"

I said, "Don't worry about it, Ruby."

She said, "But you didn't."

I said, "Okay, whatever you say," just to stop her.

The problem is she talks and talks and has to keep being busy. Because if she stops to relax or to think subjectively, she starts to cry because of her traumatic past. And everybody but herself is to blame when things go wrong, like in relationships or with people she meets. It's very sad. I would say her future is bleak (peace of mind wise) because of her history or because of her/story.

27 May

I'm feeling very lonely and cut off here in Brighton. I would like to move back to London. I felt less paranoid there and I felt safer and less lonely. But moving back would be horrendous, the stress of moving is too much to face.

2 June

The problem of writing is that you get lost in your own subjectivity and you tend to think, "this is the way the world is." I believe that could be a problem a lot of writers experience; also, artists, who are creative. But what is really true? We change from moment to moment. At the time of writing something could be true, or seem to be, but is it really? Because our perceptions change our reality changes and it changes throughout the day, week, month and year. So we are never really who we were previously.

12 June

That's probably why relationships become difficult and break up.

We need different experiences and it's the contact with other types of people that helps to give us these experiences. And helps change our consciousness and perception and gives us a deeper meaning to life and reality, which could mean spirituality.

The problem with some relationships is that one of the partners doesn't want to experience other perceptions and reality and therefore doesn't grow. That could lead to a split between them because of a lack of understanding and communication. So Spake Zarathustra, or something like that.

17 June

After all that, love is really all you need. The Beatles knew that all those years ago, when they wrote the song, *All you need is love*. After shelter and food, of course? I can understand people having pets for comfort. It helps them in their loneliness, to put their sense of love somewhere. I never understood that before.

Like a friend of mine, Fred, good old Fred, who could not understand my father committing suicide when he became ill. It wasn't until the last year of Fred's life that he said to me one day, "I understand your father doing what he did."

22 June

A friend of mine, Wayne, bought a punch bag with boxing gloves that go with it.

This is not so unusual, you might think. Well, it is really, because Wayne is very loving and you could say a sort of spiritual and kind type of guy. I suppose we all have frustrations we need to get rid of somehow. I think using a punch bag for this purpose is a good idea and I might get one myself, and pretend it is somebody I really dislike. At the moment I can't think of anybody. That's strange.

27 June

I have always been interested in why people undervalue themselves. Also, WHY people value themselves. What IS this sense of self-esteem that some have? Is it wealth, health, physical beauty, belonging to a group of like-minded people, i.e. having plenty of friends? Or is it having a marriage that works, having children, having a job that you think is important?

Or is self-esteem something deeper? A sort of inner knowing, an inner reality, that's more meaningful. Is it a trust that you know you are all right really, although you know you are far from perfect, but hopefully on a road to perfection. Dare I say, possibly, that we are spiritual beings and that deep inside ourselves there is a love that's unconditional?

Take away the biases, the anxiety, the resentments, the fears that bubble up more regularly than you desire, and beneath all that there, simmering away, is a passion of concern and a feeling of empathy for all living things. Could it be that ALL human beings have this capacity to love unconditionally. Probably not, just those that had a secure and loving childhood.

30 June

I feel very weak and spaced out. I have just recovered from a flu virus, a vicious one at that.

After the headaches have gone and uncomfortable feelings I'm left with a feeling of not really being here. Actually, it doesn't feel too bad, sort of floating in unreality. Niggling little worries don't bother me so much. I don't feel so lonely or isolated. I am able to read more, concentrate more and enjoy my trips of fantasy and imagination.

7 July

The only problem is I have had this flu virus four times since being in Brighton. I have only been here six months. In London I would probably only get it once every two years.

Also, I am on a steroid, which I wasn't in London. This tells me something: either Brighton is very polluted or something else is affecting me here.

Unhappiness, that's it. If you're unhappy you will probably become ill. Doesn't matter how beautiful the surroundings, the disease will undermine you, wear you down, deplete the immune system. You will become a victim of yourself. That's why, according to New Age ideas, you must take responsibility for your own life, your own illness, possibly your own death.

15 July

Ah, sweet death, as gentle as a mother's kiss.
Something your mother never told you about.
It comes a-calling, deceitfully, any June or July.

24 July

Five Days of Happiness?

The sun's rays sparkling, pour through the window pane.
Feeling good, feeling happy, peaceful.

Another day dawns. As morning breaks the sun shines.
Just another day.
My friend is having a nervous breakdown. I am happy.
Another is in hospital having heart surgery.
An old friend of my mother is dying of cancer.
And I am happy.

Another day dawns. The sun shines. The snow falls.
Hilary terminates her existence because she cannot bear
To be in her body with her thoughts and feelings.
It's too painful to live.
And I am feeling happy. Just another day.

A child dies somewhere in the world of malnutrition.
Swollen belly, eyes vacant.
She succumbs to death that lulls her to sleep.
Just another day and I am happy.
A terrorist plants a bomb that kills a soldier and his child.
And rejoices in the act of violence on other human beings.
Just another day and I am happy,

Remembrance Day in Flanders Fields.
The 1914-1918 War,
When humans slaughtered other humans,
Regardless of their being fellow humans.
And STILL the poppies grew in Flanders fields.

Just another day, so WHY am I happy?

Written November 1989

10 August

I don't know why I included this poem written all those
years go. I suppose it was writing about death that reminded
me of that day when it came to mind, looking through the
window of *Friends' House* in Euston, London.

It was snowing and the sun kept bursting through after the
snow stopped, making rays of light dance on my chair and
trousers. It startled me out of some sort of slumber of lost
thoughts and heaviness of body, a sort of grossness, the grav-
ity pulling me down like a giant sitting on my shoulders.

21 August

Certain sayings and quotes come to mind, like, "This
loneliness won't leave me alone." "If this is what dying is like,
I don't think much of it."

A Taoist saying, "When purpose has been used to achieve purposelessness the thing has been grasped."

And something completely different, in New York there is a saying, "You don't look people in the eye in case they turn out to be crazy."

27 August

That last word I wrote seems very symbolic. I feel like I could go crazy? I feel so frustrated and angry, a sort of inner rage that can't be subdued. I have just come in from the wind and rain; I have been caught in it four or five times today and it's just got to me.

A few weeks ago I bought a punch bag like my friend, Wayne. Punching the bag really hard for ten minutes has not relieved me, even though I feel tired.

It's still here, this inner rage . . .

2 September

As I have said before, I feel I have made a mistake coming to Brighton. How can I adapt to the situation or somehow accept I am here and enjoy being here? I can't run back to London. That situation has changed after being away for eight months.

People change. Friends move on socially and psychologically and moving is one of the most stressful of problems that people can face. I can't face it at the moment. According to EST, a Human Potential Movement, you are the source and creator of all your experience. But you, the entity that's bouncing around inside has no control of what you have created.

All you can do is "choose" what happens. When you learn to WANT what you get, you know what? You get what you want. From now on you will "always" get what you want, always . . . as long as you want what you get. Does that make sense? I hope so, because that's all I seem to be able to do at the moment. Sort of brainwash myself into believing it's okay being here.

10 September

My attempts to brainwash myself are not working. In fact, I am becoming quite sick and destructive, personally, with regard to somebody I love, because of my own inadequacy and probably low self-esteem and other problems.

Changing the subject, I was so desperate to get back to London a couple of months ago, I was considering getting married to a Russian lady who had a very nice flat in London. She was in the process of probably being deported, but I couldn't go through with it. The strain of living with her and having to move, give up my flat, my personal belongings, my own sanctuary, or prison, was too much.

What it left me with is guilt, the most dangerous of emotions. Thoughts of all my own inadequacies, of past failures, came flooding back; relationships with women, inability to finish studying, jobs or courses etc.

Stefan, my Russian friend, has not phoned me because I did not go through with the marriage. I suppose he set up the situation in the first place. He was desperate, apparently, because he loved her.

That was the only way he could get her to stay in England. We all have to pay the price of our involvement and decisions.

25 September

A couple of paragraphs back, I said I ruined a relationship because of low self-esteem.

I met this woman in Brighton, "S". We used to go to a healing group together. Over the months we got very friendly, well, sort of intimate emotionally. I started to fall in love with her because I know she had a lot of respect for me. In fact I was a little in awe of her because I suppose I had these . . . sorry to stop, but do you know, I can't write about it. I am getting uptight. I keep making mistakes on this word processor. I feel sad and angry, just writing about it. It has caused all these feelings to come to the surface, like my head is full of mush. I suddenly feel very tired. I'm going to have to stop. It's raining in my heart!

Emotions, how come they disable someone so? Where do they come from? What electric current surging through the membrane of the brain, connected to a long term memory, with a flash of deja-vu, brings a visualisation of a picture of overwhelming sadness, as though the past was suddenly brought into the present - into virtual reality, that makes one unable to function properly. Sentences keep going through my brain. "I'm a Lover that's never been kissed." "We have done no damage to our souls, to our character," Heinrich Himmler (the Gestapo chief).

Why I included that last sentence, I don't know, Gawd knows?

I don't know if I have said this before but I feel my will has been broken, some essence of togetherness inside shattered years ago. If you look closer at me, at my eyes, as you look into them, you will see a dread of life.

What I do lately is go over to the library at Whitehawk, when it's open, and read the obituaries in *The Independent* to see if anybody in there is my age.

A morbid fantasy of mine is that one day I might see my own obituary there.

20 December

I haven't written for three months, I don't know why, just unable to. Stefan and Tanya got married last week. It was me that suggested it to them, when I realised that I couldn't go through with the marriage with Tanya. Stefan at that time gave me all the reasons why HE couldn't do it. It wouldn't stop her being deported, etc. Apparently now it's not a problem for Tanya, about being deported. The Authorities only wanted her to pay for her permit * !*!*! - Good God! What have I learnt from this?

25 December

It's Christmas Day and I am alone. How does one get to this state? Is the history of rejection by my mother the cause of my isolation? Does our past create our future so completely? Are we really unable to do anything about our future? Or is loneliness a lack of love, as I once read?

I was writing this on the Downs on the edge of Whitehawk, Brighton. The wind was whistling through the branches, freezing my hands, making it hard to write. The view was wonderful, the sky so blue, the sun was out and there was a lovely warmth from it, making me feel a sort of painless euthanasia of my feelings, even making me feel sort of mystical. Perhaps that's what junkies get when they take heroin.

I long for the return of the old feelings that I used to have, especially when I am one with nature. I only get this feeling when I have been alone for a long period of time.

I have not been able to write for about three months, since I had all that turmoil with Stefan and Tanya and the emotional dependence on "S". It's all changed now with "S". In fact I think I could grow to resent having met her, because of my own inadequacy.

This is so self-indulgent.

26 December

Maybe I shouldn't have gone on the Downs yesterday, because my asthma has suddenly come on today, Boxing Day.

Stefan phoned me last night, which was very nice. He is happily married. Information I have had from other sources tells me he has calmed down a lot. He was in a state because his brother was shot last year in Russia. It's a shock like this, probably, that makes one realise that life is really only very short, so what's the use of getting too uptight about it? The trouble is, it doesn't last, we soon forget, and then get caught up in all the crap of ourselves and others.

Can it really be a year since I wrote about last Christmas or didn't write, so to speak, because it was so horrendous? This year is just as bad; it's just that I am more able to write about it.

28 December

I sit at my word processor and stare at the cursor, blinking on and off on the line, waiting for something to come into my thoughts. Something that's relevant to what? Life I suppose.

30 December

I'm bored, bored, bloody bored. Now that's a funny thing, as Max Miller would say, "boredom," what does it mean? It's an emotional state of being unable to concentrate on any one given thing, so one flits from one thing to another. In fact, I believe it goes deeper than that. I believe it's a state of disturbance. The emotional state underneath makes one unable to concentrate on any one given subject. Could be sadness, or grief, or anger. Or some deep emotional hurt from way back in one's history that disables the person.

1996
Brighton

Happy New Year! ?

2 January

The problem of low self-esteem seems to be in vogue. Princess Diana spoke about it on the TV programme, *Panorama*. She spoke about her difficulties with her marriage to Prince Charles. It was also on the front page of the *Big Issue*, the street magazine for the homeless and also on the TV programme, *Kilroy*, which was about self-mutilation and low self-esteem concerning women.

Is this a malaise of contemporary society or is it just a media hyped word? Maybe it's just a condition of human existence. High and low self-esteem, treat these two impostors just the same.

5 January

I was reading about a pop star, saying he doesn't belong to so-called "society." He felt like an outsider, with a chip on his shoulder, sort of thing. I suddenly realised there must be millions of people out there, feeling the same thing as I do, and he does. Only difference is, apparently, the amount of affairs he is supposed to be having with women. He doesn't feel out of place there; I should be so lucky. An old Jewish saying.

7 January

Actually, I feel I want to be an outsider, to feel I am

different. It gives me a sense of importance and feels familiar. Like my childhood, it feels safer because it's familiar. - Actually, I am writing this to the background sound of Frankie Lane, singing *Jealousy*. It's a problem I think I may have. He sings with such feeling it brings out emotional feelings in me as I rock to and fro to the music and write this.

Yes, I believe I am happy in this state of being, isolated from others. When I try and get back to being accepted socially it doesn't seem to work. Maybe they feel this energy of isolation in my demeanour and reject me just like I wanted. And I run away and complain about "them bastards," but in fact I am creating my own reality. Like, I know, I am different and they know I am different. Full stop.

It's pointless trying to hide one's negative feelings about oneself, because people pick it up. They know something is wrong, even if they can't define it.

15 February

There should be a book written on how to survive Brighton. One thing I have found out is that you don't take it, or even the people, too seriously.

That might sound like a harsh thing to say, but that is the nature of the beast. What I mean is, it's a hello, goodbye, sort of town, tinsel town.

The people who live here, or who have made their life here, probably live very varied lives, and are into all sorts of activities outside their own domesticities - things like dancing, singing, writing groups, yoga, t'ai chi, religious groups, psychology meetings, humanist groups, the state of the nation groups, moral and ethical groups. There are healing groups, psychic groups, political discussion groups, old age discussion groups, gender bender groups, gay groups, social issue groups, single people meeting groups, history of Brighton groups. Musicians even perform in other people's houses, for a small fee. If you're into creativity, the scope is enormous in Brighton.

A lot of the people attending these groups are married, but people are coming and going all the time. The transience of the place is obvious. Brighton is a place of people in transit.

There is always a shoulder to cry on, to tell your story to. You think you are important to somebody, and they are important to you. You then find that they have many friends just as important. You are just another face, another body, not really needed. People flirt with each other, I don't just mean sexually. You make friends easily, and they leave you just as easily, and it doesn't mean anything. I don't mean they really leave you, just that you stop contacting each other, as though you are all sort of tired or bored, and need somebody else who is new and exciting. You will talk, if you see them in the street, but usually that's all.

There is a sort of warmth about Brighton, a sort of warm superficiality. It's probably one of the most accepting of towns, and one of the least judgemental. It's just that people who live here all the year round see so many different ideas of how people live, dress and look. Anything goes, as I explained earlier, with so many people doing their own thing that they really don't have enough time for people outside their own group, busy, busy. Unless, they feel, "There is something interesting for me here." All this in about two or three miles radius, houses crammed together, spilling over each other.

21 February

Because Brighton has a very tolerant attitude to all kinds of people you might think it sounds an ideal and exciting place, but there is a price to pay for this, and that is that there is a feeling of no real depth to anything. Easy come, easy go. Maybe it's because the tourist atmosphere prevails here, and that has affected the residents.

I notice that misfits seem to feel at home here. They always seem to have a companion to talk to, male or female, integrated together. I see young women with older men, drinking cans of beer on the streets, deep in conversation, sitting anywhere - even on the ground. It's a very impulsive environment. People are easily distracted by what's going on around them.

Brighton opens people up, but because of the atmosphere, it's difficult for them to come down or close down. Because of this, they can become susceptible to a lot of divergent activities, at a cost to their mental stability.

There's a feeling of emotionally incestuous behaviour and this is a problem of the free-and-easyness of Brighton. People become too close too soon, and open up about their personal lives. They then reveal more of themselves to each other, sometimes doubting if they should have done so.

26 February

Brighton is full of characters. A woman I met, called Daisy Prince, runs an amateur theatre company in Sussex Gardens, and puts on plays and pantomimes two or three times a year. It's apparently been going for fifty years. I don't know if she has been running it for that long, but she might well have been. I thought her name, Daisy Prince, was a stage name, but it's her real name. What else could she do with a name like that, but be an actress?

1 March

There is only but one truly serious philosophical problem. And that is suicide.

Judging whether life is, or is not, worth living amounts to answering the fundamental question of philosophy. All the rest, whether or not the world has three dimensions, whether the mind has nine or twelve categories comes after. These are games. They do not answer the fundamental question.

Albert Camus

Just read that Margot Hemmingway has committed suicide. She was the grand-daughter of Ernest Hemingway, the writer, who also committed suicide.

Some uncles and an aunt also committed suicide. Apparently, they all drank heavily, even the last casualty, Margot. Is it in the genes?

The main cause of mental illness is a feeling of alienation. Why should anybody alienate themselves willingly? Humans are basically gregarious animals. It's more probably unwillingly. The feelings are, I believe, those of self- preservation. In order not to be overwhelmed by feelings of inadequacy in the company of others some people prefer their own company to socially mingling with others. The problem with this is that the more you alienate yourself, the more difficult it becomes to integrate. You lose social skills, even such little things as acknowledging other people. Or, as is becoming more common these days, you integrate into a subculture of drugs and drink. Squatting seems to reflect this, as well as providing shelter. It brings people together who, with their very homelessness, have a feeling of sharing their alienation.

You could see this happening in the spaces underneath the Royal Festival Hall in London, where people made their homes back in the seventies. They had beds, blankets, wardrobes, cabinets, crockery, heating facilities and so on. It was like an open-air home. Westminster Council cleared them out because it was affecting the tourist trade of Westminster.

7 March

I feel very low, and I am trying to rise above depression and apathy. I lost ten pages of writing on my word processor. I put a television too near this word processor and it affected the floppy disk's magnetic recording and erased the ten pages. I find writing very stressful. Those ten pages were difficult to write, all about what I see going on around me here in Brighton.

11 March

I keep thinking about the ten pages I lost. There was some good stuff in them. I have to somehow mentally accept they are gone, and let it be, let the past go, so I can always start afresh, to be in the present.

Can we, as human beings, with a brain that is so powerful and yet so little understood, erase our history so we don't become destroyed by it, and only keep the positive parts that make us feel good - the memories of love, affection, fun and laughter? I hope so, but I must admit it's a struggle, and as I am writing this, I keep slipping back to thoughts and paragraphs that I wrote. My experiences of what happened to me, what I observed as the invisible man, an Urban Robinson Crusoe, a walking video camera.

22 March

There seems to be a change of language that probably reflects the times. We don't, apparently, fall in love any more, we fall in lust. This must mean we have lost something, lost some romantic ideal about men and women's fantasies about romantic relationships, that makes one's feeling of "aaahhh" come to the surface. And it seems men are bringing cases to court regarding sexual discrimination. Some sort of backlash against feminism, perhaps? These were considered women's issues only a few years ago.

I thought I must seem attractive the other day, when I was sitting near the window of a restaurant, having a cup of coffee. Young women kept looking at me through the window, until I realised they were looking at reflections of themselves.

14 April

I joined *Brights,* an organisation that swaps skills in a barter context, no money involved.

Since joining, I have had three massages from a woman who advertised that she needed bodies to work on, so she got mine. The experience was wonderful. Her name is Maria, a beautiful Polish woman. When she finishes, she always asks me what I am doing afterwards, and I say something of what I am doing.

When she asks me, I always think that I have a chance with her. But I realise many people say this in Brighton, as a means of communication.

"What are you doing to-day?" is, I suppose, to get some ideas for themselves. They usually tell you anyway. Over the Easter period she asked me the same question, and I said, "Oh, nothing really." I asked her what she was doing, and she said, "Nothing," I said, "Oh?" and left.

7 June

It's been months since I've written anything, not able to concentrate.

I had a chance to go back to London. I was offered a flat in East Finchley, a nice flat, nice estate, nice area. I wanted to go, but couldn't cope with the idea of moving, the stress it would involve, my state of mind.

All the things I have to do are coming at me all at once, creating a whirlwind of thoughts that reach a crescendo of absolute panic. So I had to refuse, even though I was offered help.

The indecision caused so much anxiety and depression that I became very ill with a bodily weakness, a sort of ME. I also got sciatica, a terrible back pain and arthritis. This was an attack of acute arthritis. I really feel empathy for people suffering from this complaint, the pain is atrocious.

13 June

I blamed myself unmercifully, blamed people, blamed Brighton, fell out with people. My feelings towards myself were undermining and unbalancing me. God, why do we do these things to ourselves? I projected my feelings onto "S".

She felt hurt, all because of my inadequacy and rage.

I said goodbye to a woman I had known for fifteen years who has a partner in Devon. We used to phone each other regularly. I don't know why we keep in touch. She had a partner, and it had become a lot different in the last few years. I felt she wasn't keen, really, to keep communicating, after she failed to phone back three times, when it was her turn to call me. I felt very angry about it. I wrote a goodbye letter to her, then she suddenly phoned and was upset by it. We were very close once, but it all changed when she had a partner. She thinks she will miss me, but she won't, not that much, not really. She once said she felt better knowing I'm here, in the world, alive, even if she didn't see me. What does it mean?

17 June

I want to try and recall some of the ten pages I wrote. One thing I remember is my experiment with visualisation. I used to go to London at least once a week, and coming back one week I felt bored, so I tried to imagine a beautiful woman sitting next to me. Nothing happened for a while, and then the train started to fill up with passengers. All of a sudden I heard a voice say to me, "Excuse me." It was a beautiful woman, a "starlet," asking me to move my bag, so she could sit down. I couldn't believe it! She sat next to me all the way to Brighton, even though other seats became vacant. In fact, when some of the men passengers were getting off, they stared at her, and then at me, probably thinking, "What's that beautiful woman doing with that odd-looking character?" I started to get nervous, because she was falling asleep and her head was nearly on my shoulder. The carriage was practically empty when we arrived in Brighton. I wanted to say something, but I didn't, because I felt it would spoil the fantasy.

24 June

The following week, on another trip from London back to

Brighton, I thought I would try it again. What happened was this. A woman sat next to me, who I would say was attractive in a way, and also two young women sat to my right on the opposite seat. They looked at me a couple of times. But my fantasy was always of being with a single beautiful woman.

Weighing up the visualisation experiment and trying to consider if it was successful or not, I think, well, not really.

The train pulled into the station. The man opposite me got up and left the train. Looking out of the window, I saw a very attractive woman sitting on a seat on the platform. She had a sort of fur coat and a very short skirt, very sexy. Sort of a high-class call girl. I noticed her on the seat as the train came into the station. I actually thought she was waiting for another train.

I thought this visualisation wasn't going to work, because I saw no beautiful women getting on the train, when all of a sudden the woman on the platform came and sat opposite me and smiled. She sat down and crossed her beautiful legs. I sort of smiled back, feeling very coy. She started to read a book, leaning forward a little. I didn't know what to do. She had long black hair and a petite face, but she looked very streetwise. I think she was aware I was nervous - she actually looked up from reading her book a couple of times and smiled.

All the way to Brighton I was transfixed, wondering if I had created this. Two out of two. Is it possible that we can create our own reality? What, happened was, again, I never said anything, even though I wanted to.

I got off the train first and she followed behind, clipping, clopping, with her high heels. I realised I had lost her, so I slowed down and waited for her to catch up. As I came near the exit I pretended to look at the indicator board and looked across to the right, hoping to see her. Then I saw her. She looked right across the station at me. I was a bit startled by it - ships in the night, strangers on a train, or even brief encounter?

2 July

I'm in a pub, *The Bristol,* at the bottom of Paston Street, Kemptown, another part of Brighton. I'm facing the seafront. I think I'm invisible. Nobody sees me. I have grown a beard again. I feel safer hiding behind it. I haven't been in a pub for ages. I feel this double rum and pepsi beginning to have an effect. I am becoming warm and relaxed, listening to the mutterings of conversations wafting over me from all directions, everybody believing what they have to say is so important.

This biro I'm using - the ink keeps stopping coming through, sort of keeps drying up, even though there is ink in it. But if I imagine energy running down my arm to the pen, it starts to work every time. I have done this dozens of times. I keep this biro just to see if I can keep it writing by imagination, just to see if I can do it again and again, and it always works.

I noticed after a couple of drinks that I couldn't write with the pen. Maybe I became too relaxed, and that special energy that causes the effect became unavailable. This is the first time I have tried it after drinking, and the first time it hasn't worked. This shows that alcohol destroys the power of thought. We must surely create a force with our thoughts. I am sure this can be proved scientifically.

16 July

A Day in London

I'm back in Camden for the day. I'm in the Royal Free Hospital, where I used to go and write when I lived in London. I've just come for a cup of coffee in the out-patients' cafeteria, and it's very quiet.

I am staying in my friend's flat, free from the strains and stresses of Brighton, while he is staying in mine in Brighton, for a break by the sea, free from the strains and stresses of London.

To the left of where I'm sitting there are two old ladies. They are together, but they are not sitting together. One is sitting in front of the other, on a separate table. One of the ladies turns round to the other to talk, and the first one replies. There is enough room for both to sit together, but it seems they have decided not to. The one sitting behind gets up, asks her friend if she wants a cup of coffee. She replies she does, and offers to pay. The one behind refuses her offer, and there is a discussion about who should pay. The one behind, slowly walking to the counter, says, "Wait there. I'll get them." The one sitting down says, "Why did you say that? I'm not going anywhere." My imagination, and presumption, is that they probably come here every day and go through these rituals.

One of these seems to be taking place while I watch. The one in front is reading from a newspaper and commenting about the news to the one behind, who sometimes can't hear or understand her comments.

The one in front gets annoyed a couple of times when her friend fails to understand what she is saying. I think she isn't really listening because she seems to be staring into space with a sad look on her face, as if she's going way back, back into time, to some forgotten era when she felt needed, and belonged to a society she understood, that wasn't alien and incomprehensible to her. They leave together, the sad one trailing behind the one who was sitting in front, walking as they were sitting, one behind the other.

18 July

It's 6.30 am. I tried to write last night, but I was unable to. I felt apathetic and had no energy again. The weather is so muggy. I really tried, but had no will or imagination, two things that Colin Wilson, the writer, seems to think you need to be creative. Faculty X he calls it. I had no will, was unable to concentrate.

But this morning, I feel so different. I must admit that I

seem to be a morning person. I always feel optimistic in the morning, the start of a new day. Anything's possible. I feel we have so many options to be who we want to be. Does this sound like schizophrenia, or even multiphrenia?

It gives me a lot of excitement. I am feeling excited writing this, sort of shaking with keenness and awareness. The difference from last night is amazing! Why are we unable to tap into this energy at will? I do try, and at times I am able to, and I think I have mastered it.

But when I try it at some other time, like last night, I am unable to. I really tried to get my will to work, sat at the word processor. I wrote a couple of lines, erased them, tried again, a couple of lines ... nothing! I felt very frustrated, and gave up.

Wondering why I couldn't do it, I went to bed and watched the Olympics. I marvelled at the athleticism and will of the athletes. It was really humid and muggy there in Atlanta, much worse than here. Were they able to create some energy, or dig deep into their psyche to find a sense of power and will to compete? Or was it only the winners who were able to do this?

19 July

Last night, I wanted to write about the Unemployed Centre in Tilbury Place, where I have decided to do some voluntary work. If you want a nervous breakdown, that's the place to work.

It was set up about fifteen years ago for unemployed people to help themselves. I don't know how they financed it originally. I believe the unemployed did it themselves somehow. I will have to find out, but now they have a grant from the National Lottery. It's a place, I would say, where the people who run it are generally altruistic, and want to help. There's a welfare advice office where people drop in for any aspect of welfare advice free of charge. There's a crèche, and they have people volunteering their skills for classes. These include writing groups, yoga, painting, dancing, computing, teaching foreign languages, t'ai chi, guitar lessons, environmental issues, and they sell natural (organic) food. This is all wonderful, but the problem is it's chaotic!

They have a very democratic system, where everybody has a right to express an opinion, even the volunteers. But this leads to a sort of anarchy with people thinking their thing, or they themselves, are the most important. People don't listen to each other. It becomes manic and crazy. There seem to be power struggles between the paid workers and volunteers. Things get lost or misplaced, people just walk in the office any time for information, or a chat, or to express a grievance while you are counting the incoming money, the float, or maybe petty cash and the money from courses.

You are suddenly surrounded by people you don't know and, as the office is so small, trying to concentrate on what you are doing becomes a great feat of endurance. I have seen women crying, men shouting, dirty coffee cups lying around for days, bits of paper stuck up here, there and everywhere, about this meeting, that political event, that change in the organisation. Now and again there's a purge to get rid of all of the notices that have become out-of-date. There's a smell of cigarette smoke wafting all over the place.

They have meetings for this, meetings for that, emergency meetings maybe for some incident that's cropped up, or for some interdepartmental quarrel that's arising. Some volunteer told me she used to be a paid worker, but left because she felt she was having a nervous breakdown.

Apparently, now there is some problem with somebody accusing someone else of mismanagement and corruption to do with the financing of the centre.

In spite of all that, I still have to say that it's a friendly place, and I believe people are basically trying to help each other, themselves and the underprivileged. And I don't mean from the petty cash.

22 July

Where I live, there are a lot of single parents. I see these very young women walking down the street with young children in prams. The women seem just out of school.

The young woman who lives opposite me was a single mother, and the woman who came after she left is also a single parent. I hear her screaming at the child nearly all the time, day or night. I hear that they are going to slash single mothers' benefit. If we think this is a big social problem, I read that in the 1914-18 war they were very concerned about single mothers. It seems that so many men were slaughtered, numbers running into millions, that it's not surprising that there were unmarried mothers. The men were never able to get back to marry them.

25 July

In Brighton, there are so many women around, young and old. I am sure the women outnumber the men, especially in the summer, when you get the foreign students, mostly young women.

The numbers seem to treble. If you can't get a woman in Brighton, you can't get a woman anywhere, but what does that say about me, an unconfirmed bachelor?

Two young men I know who don't have girlfriends, and who have lived here for years, are both very creative and perform in musical groups, playing guitars and writing their own material. You would somehow think they would have the opportunities to be able to get a woman. They said, "It's not us that don't want relationships, it's the women. They want to have a good time and don't want a regular partner."

A friend who runs Egyptian dancing groups has plenty of young women coming to her groups. She said that most of them don't have boyfriends. It seems strange to me that either the men or the women don't want relationships. I think it's Brighton - it's so distracting to young people. Too many goodies around.

The men I spoke to said it's a sort of "Look, don't touch."

attitude, and the women seem to think the men don't want the responsibility of a serious relationship. Maybe this is taking "doing your own thing" too far. The people who want a relationship want a partner to fit into how they want to live. And there is no-one around who fits that criterion.

27 July

I see that a certain museum is selling packets of dust to visitors because the dust may have fallen on famous ornaments or paintings. God, how can we take anything seriously from the media when we get this sort of ridiculous news poured out? Or should we be more concerned about the people who are buying the packets of dust?

30 July

I have noticed we are becoming a nation of appointment makers. It is a social must now, to have your Filofax on you, so you can fit people into your agenda.

"Yes, I can see you. Will the 8th of January, year 2003, at 2.00 p.m. do? Oh, by the way, I apologise if I am a bit late. I have a dental appointment at 1.30 p.m, and by the way, Happy Millennium!"

1 August

I know a couple of women, and when I was with them when I first came to Brighton, I noticed they would not go in certain shops. I asked them why, and they said they didn't like the person serving, so they would go out of their way to go to another similar shop, just to avoid them.

At the time, I couldn't understand it, just coming from London. Going into shops is so impersonal. You are one of the probably thousands of customers. In a smaller town I suppose feelings become more personalised. I wonder what happens in a small village where there is only one grocer and you fall out with him. I suppose you have to go to the next village or town if you want groceries.

But I have noticed that after being here for eighteen months, I don't go to certain shops, mainly ones that do photocopies. For some reason I have fallen out with the people in these shops, usually about how the copies come out, so I go out of my way to go to another copy shop. Good job there are plenty of photocopy shops around!

Where I live in the Whitehawk area there are two working men's cafés that I don't go into anymore. The first week I moved here I went to both of them, but I didn't like the people's attitudes in them - very abrupt - and the atmosphere in the cafés was full of tension. Parts of where I live are very rough. It's known as a rough area, and people don't want to move to this particular area. They actually name Whitehawk as an area they don't want to go to when they are seeking to exchange flats (through the local council or housing associations). I'm lucky that where I live it's relatively quiet.

5 August

I have just seen two headlines on the news posters. One was, "LONDON, THIS STINKING CITY. GET THE GUARDIAN THIS WEEKEND!" The other was "BRIGHTON'S HOSPITALS, THIS PLAGUE OF VIOLENCE! GET THE BRIGHTON ARGUS." I must go to the library, Monday, to get back copies and try and read what these headlines are all about. Doesn't really surprise me. I have been very aware, and so have a lot of people, about these statements. Aware, because I worked in London, in a casualty hospital in the 1970s. It was quite violent then, but not as I would presume it is now. Probably much worse.

8 August

On a train to London recently, an oldish couple sat opposite me. They seemed a wealthy couple. The man was a large man, the woman seemed the appropriate height for him. I sensed something was wrong, and very quickly I realised the woman had such disdain for him. The man was trying to get her attention, showing her articles in the newspaper he was reading. She was not interested and kept turning her head away from him as she was reading a book. I would guess they were married and by now shouldn't have been.

She never said a word and kept pulling her arm away when he touched her. He must have tried about half a dozen times to get her attention. Her look was enough and there was a lot said in that look. She hated him.

20 August

This Brighton, this crazy unreal town can take a well-adjusted person to the edge, and does!

A woman I was having a casual conversation with said she was attracted to a man she met who had just moved to Brighton, an accountant. What attracted her was his stability of nature, and even his conservative outlook.

After two years living together in Brighton, he changed from this straight guy to a hippie-type beatnik. He fixed himself up with an ear-ring, wore way out clothes, started smoking pot, grew a beard, let his hair grow. She said, she was sure it was Brighton that had affected him. Because of the way he had changed they split up.

People who move to Brighton encounter people of different social backgrounds and experiences, who are thrown together into a manic whirligig of activity. The heart of Brighton is the area roughly about a three mile radius from the Palace Pier back to Kemptown, across to Elm Grove, down to Kensington Gardens, up to Brighton Station, up to Seven Dials and down to Norfolk Square.

If you have moved to Brighton from other parts of England, or for that matter from abroad or from outer space, you will meet people and probably become acquainted with people you would not generally mix with from whence you came.

Amongst these might be gay men and women, skinheads, students, travellers, New Agers, hippies, tourists, criminals, people of the third age, beggars, well-off people retiring here, writers (like yours truly?), musicians, poets, healers, Quakers, overspill from London, and wanderers not knowing where they want to be. If somebody walked down the street naked, people in Brighton wouldn't be too perturbed by it. And if an alien walked down the street here I doubt if they would even notice. They would think he was just a typical Brighton wally.

Now this is good, you might say, creates a vibrant and varied community. But Brighton, being a magnet for people escaping from their problems the downside is that it has the largest proportion of homeless people of any town in Great Britain.

1 October

People come up to you and start talking and you're not sure what they're talking about. There is a community but it feels unstable, transient, enticing, exhilarating even. That's why tourists and day-trippers love it. There is, because of this forced acceptance of others, an impatience with others.

We have misunderstanding with our friends, who are on our wave length, never mind somebody who is from another planet.

I have been wondering why people are so up-tight in Brighton. I can understand it in London, it's obvious. WHY Brighton? What is this irritable atmosphere that pervades under the surface? I believe it's partly impatience, but why are people impatient? Perhaps because they don't feel safe they are not really relating. People are accepting but where is the belonging?

People have, for their own reasons, an expectation about Brighton. Might it fulfil some need they feel they have? All sense of personal control seems to go. Their energy flows out impulsively, as though it's their right. Because this is Brighton anything goes here, anything. And when this need is not fulfilled they feel let down, thwarted even.

I believe a lot become very frustrated and disillusioned. They either leave, or stay and add to the other thousands of flotsam and jetsam that inhabit the town, lost in the fantasy of unreality that Brighton creates, to the detriment of their own mental and emotional stability.

If you have to use the buses a lot you will notice that people talk to each other as though other people were not around. You're trapped in your seat, forced to hear this idle gossip, tittle-tattle. You can hear every word, whole life stories, abound around you. Generally it's a criticism of people they know or have met. Running other people down seems to be the recreation of people in Brighton.

7 October

I can't get over the emotional intensity that Brighton seems to create. It's amazing what I have heard. Impulsively animated, Brighton people talk as though there was nobody else around, projecting their own insecurities and frustrations on others.

8 October

The next morning after writing that about the buses, two young women were behind me on a number 44 bus going from Whitehawk down to Elm Grove, talking about their hen night with a male stripper. All their intimate details were there. I kept looking round so they were aware I could hear everything they were saying, hoping they would stop. Not a bit, they just went on talking, oblivious of anybody else. At the same time I had this young kid in front of me, staring right in my face, making faces at me. This is 8.30 in the morning. I suppose this is what it's like being in a mad-house, living in close proximity, unable to escape from the other inmates.

This is not a rare experience in Brighton. It's a regular occurrence. Later at the post office, two old ladies of the third age were running down some woman as I was waiting to be served. I nearly made a comment about it to them. I have rarely been aware of this sort of unpleasantness in London.

Before I really knew Brighton, some people told me that one gets caught up in all this hype and then gradually gets worn down by it and have to back off. This definitely seems to be the pattern of people who attend the unemployed centre in Tilbury Place.

Even I must admit that they try and do good work and help people who are in unfortunate circumstances, but the stress there does accumulate to unbearable levels sometimes with tensions between people, and accusations flying around.

17 November

I think I am becoming peopled out, an expression I picked up reading a therapy book some time ago. It says what it means, meeting too many people and becoming worn out by it.

The energy we need to maintain our sense of equilibrium gets drained from us by running around, trying to meet all these people, doing all this socialising, out of some fear of being alone. For myself, I did all this socialising out of fear of not being able to be a sociable human being. I am an observer, a cortex camera, a person looking in. I am an audience, not a partaker or player in this business of existence that people call real life.

I suppose I am like the three characters in the Wizard of Oz: the scarecrow, the lion and the tin man. The first has no brain, the second no courage, the third and probably most crucial, no heart. Can one purchase these in our consumerist society or does one have these given as gifts?

24 December

I have received twenty Christmas cards and I haven't sent one. This is the second year I have done this. I gave the money to a charity that I would have spent on Christmas cards and stamps. I have had terrible Christmases in the past, spent alone like RC on his island, yet I have had at least a dozen cards. Seems pointless sending any, or am I not getting into the Christmas spirit? Am I lacking any spirit of festivity? Oh humbug!

Possibly I might be haunted by Scrooge tonight, Christmas Eve, and be whisked back to Christmases past and into future Christmases, because of the results of my actions. And I might wake up tomorrow with a different attitude and start enjoying myself and give all my money away to the first Tiny Tim-type character that I meet. Funnily enough the money I gave to charity instead of Christmas cards, was to the disabled children's charity. So the gods might relent tonight and give me peace.

28 December

Why is it more prose-writers go mad and commit suicide than poets? Poetry exists, I believe, in a higher state of mind. It comes from the soul, from nature and from love. It's inspired, a state of grace which comes from "letting go and letting it flow."

Prose is earned. You dig deep. It's tiring, frustrating, it's a means to an end, a commitment and schedule. It requires a concentrated will and dogged determination.

30 December

I suppose some writers suffer from a nervous and anxious temperament. I wonder if they should write if it's going to cost them their sanity. Is it worth it? Readers and publishers would probably say yes to that question. Or do they do it out of a feeling they have something to say and it's important and interesting what they say?

They must believe that, otherwise they are deceiving themselves and it's pointless writing. "Oh what a tangled web we weave when first we practise to deceive." - Sir Walter Scott.

31 December

The truth can drive us twice as mad.

Now that I agree with. It's a dangerous game, truth, subjective or absolute. Especially truthful introspection.

1997
Brighton

Happy New Year?

2 January

I was reading a book by a woman writer whose name I have
forgotten. The book was about her own experience of writing.
She went off somewhere to write in solitude for a year and I
believe the book was actually called *Solitude*. She wrote:

> The burden of mystery must be with him day and night.
> He must be shaken by the truth that will not be comforted.
> This divine discontent, this disequilibrium, this state of
> inner tension, is the source of artistic energy.
>
> Many lesser poets have it only in their youth, some, even
> of the greatest, lose it in middle life. Wordsworth lost the
> courage to despair and with it his poetic power. But more
> often, the dynamic tensions are so powerful that they
> destroy the man before he reaches maturity.

6 January

I wish I had written that. I don't believe in destroying
oneself for art, for a sort of creative martyrdom.

But isn't it best to try and be creative and say your piece,
maybe in artistic form, even if you're prone to despair and
depression, and not be one of millions of victims in our society
who suffer low self-esteem, depression and despair, and don't
do anything, who go out with a whimper and not a bang. God
bless them.

My desire is to be objective and not just subjective, so people will read what I write and hopefully get something out of it. We all need to aspire/be inspired time after time.

7 January

Writing is a lonely existence, staring at a blank piece of paper or screen. It's also an indulgence of thoughts and feelings, with a process of hope that to write about what we see and feel will relieve us of inner tensions and unwanted thoughts, creating a cathartic effect for our soul to be at peace.

9 January

Future?

Is there a future, an on-going task, an existence, a performance for a body that walks the streets of Brighton and London, that observes, that recollects, that records the happenings that go on before its eyes? Who are the people? Are they just bodies, mirages or phantoms that appear? The others, that authorise our existence? That believe they're real? Their energies, their cells, their material, are they real? Do they really exist?

I feel I will try and go back to London and become anonymous. I am becoming too well-known here. Return and become the real Urban Robinson Crusoe . . .

10 June

Six months with no inclination to write. I have decided to split with "J", the woman I have been physically and emotionally involved with after being together for six months. I felt the relationship wasn't going anywhere. Anyway she kept making excuses not to see me, but deep down I am not sure why I did finish the relationship.

About a week before I said goodbye, I had a feeling of complete and utter boredom with everything. I felt I have no problem, no worries. I even felt that I was very lucky compared to a lot of other people who are homeless, sick, have financial worries, or are in difficult marriages.

So I am wondering, why did I finish with this woman? Was it to create a problem for myself, by being alone, having to survive without her, because however difficult the relationship was, she tried to support me in her own way.

I believe subconsciously I finished it to create a challenge for myself. To be alone in the world might make me more creative, try and write again, feel my isolation and my sense of being an outsider.

Was I feeling too safe? Do I need to feel hurt and pain to be creative, to be able to express myself? It definitely feels more familiar. Is that familiarity more secure for me, even though it's negative? Am I like millions of people who prefer negativity rather than positive feelings, just because we are more able to cope with them?

It seems we are unable to love for too long. Love makes us feel unsafe because its unfamiliar and dangerous. We can't stand too much of it!

BORING: maybe it's that I am just boring myself, or that I am a boring person. This reminds me of another famous writer who actually wrote about boredom. Kierkegaard, the Norwegian, writer, philosopher and mystic. He wrote:

> The Gods were bored, so they created man. Adam was bored, so Eve was created. Adam was bored alone, then Adam and Eve were bored together. Then Adam and Eve and Cain and Able their offspring were bored as a family. Then the population of the world increased, and the people were bored en masse. To divert themselves, they conceived the idea of constructing a tower high enough to reach the heavens. This idea itself is as boring as the tower was high, and constitutes a terrible proof, of how boredom had gained the upper hand.

That's so wonderfully boring.

15 June

I know, and have met many people in Brighton. Characters abound here. Maybe it's because people become themselves in Brighton. You face yourself. It's a town where you can let go, so it all gets revealed. You can't escape and your real personality becomes open to others over a period of time.

You keep bumping into all sorts of characters in town over the weeks and months even years. You mention somebody, and then you realise other people know them or have met them, doing the rounds or events that are happening in town, or you get introduced to others because of your own interests. Doesn't matter what interests it would be, from writer's groups, to computer and internet classes, humanists' gatherings, alcohol interests, drugs. You will find your own social whirl, and it all happens in a short time.

One character is Alex, a writer, who I believe is, or could be a great novelist. He has a great style of writing: his manuscript that he has been carrying around with him for years, mainly written while he was on the road, is a fantasy based on his experiences of the people he met there. The personalities, the good the bad and ugly, are all there in the book.

Apparently it's based on Capitalism v Communism with goblins, wizards, castles, surreal towns and different dimensions. Probably, I think he would say, it's not like that but like this. This goblin relates to so and so who we might know. He might be a dodgy character, or this is somebody else who is a fair minded person, etc.

The manuscript is a great philosophical concept of life, society and people. It should be published when it's finished. If he is determined I think it will be.

London
Camden Again

Descent into Madness

26 August

Another huge twist to Urban Robinson Crusoe. I am back in London. I had an offer I really couldn't refuse, a one bedroom flat in St John's Wood, a very select part of London. It's near Primrose Hill and Regents Park. It's so strange being here after my emotional life was turned upside down by being by Brighton for two and a half years. I am not the same person coming back to London and feel lost and bewildered. I hope I can gain some control over my state of mind. I have been here a month.

12 October

England qualified for the World Cup last night. I watched the match on TV. Freddie Starr is getting old, but he still made me laugh even though some of his antics are outrageous and pathetic.

Jeffrey Bernard is dead. He was a journalist who had a column in one of the daily papers for donkeys' years, and whose real claim to fame is his drunkenness in a pub he used to frequent in Soho where the landlord used to tolerate him, probably the only landlord in Soho who would. He was so famous because of his drinking they made a play about him, which I have forgotten the name of. And that reminds me, I keep forgetting things. - How's that for a contradiction?

I also watched two TV biographies of the slow deterioration of two famous artists, one a writer, Jack Kerouac, the other an actor, Montgomery Clift. Both became addicted to booze and drugs. I could have gone that way years ago. So far I have always have been able to avoid that situation but lately I think I am coming to the end of my resistance to them. It's as though I would like to go mad, not the madness of terrible hallucinations, but the madness of indifference and get into a sort of catatonic state of mind, or even become happy mad. This is to escape from samsara. (Samsara is the Hindu idea of the endless cycle of birth, death, and rebirth. As I see it this is the world of secular life, society, other people.)

As the Buddhists would say, Bodhisattvas (who are angels apparently) protect me from the awesome and fearsome realm of samsara.

15 October

If I am to go mad, I might as well write about it and try and be creative with it.

The first people to become aware that you are different are strangers. They look at you surreptitiously or avoid looking at you at all. They either stare, or they actually don't see you because, subconsciously, they don't want to. Like the time I met a friend in a coffee bar in Regents Park Road. When I went in the café my friend Geoffrey was the only one sitting in there, so I walked in. I ordered a coffee. After about twenty minutes I realised I never had my coffee, so I called the waitress over and asked her if she heard me order. She said she did, but she forgot. I wouldn't mind if the café was crowded but it wasn't. There was only Geoff and me.

People tend to get irritated by you when you're around in the streets. Once a woman said to me one day when it was pouring with rain, "You should go that way," as though I was in her way. I was nowhere near her.

And in a supermarket when I wanted to buy a packet of green cigarette papers the girl asked who was next so I walked up and said, "A packet of green cigarette papers, please." I asked how much because I forgot things a lot at that time and she really shouted "EIGHTEEN PENCE!" No "please," or "thank you," when I gave her the money. So I hung around to see if she was just like that normally or if that was a part of her nature.

She was nice as pie to the next customer and he happened to be black. In these days when there is still a lot of prejudice in this country against black people it seems that there is actually even more prejudice against people who are mad.

You also notice children stare at you while they are with their mothers. One mother with her child dragging her along by her hand kept looking around at me. I had to cross the road, to get out of the way. Fancy being afraid of a little child. I actually realise why a lot of people who go mad think they're Jesus. It's because they feel persecuted just like him.

People try to intimidate you. I had three incidents in two days. I hadn't had any before, and I had been here for three months. It's only these last two or three days I have been feeling very fragmented and out of it. I can't clean my flat, can't decide what to eat or which bill to pay, or concentrate on anything for too long.

19 October

People really frighten me, especially crowds. Their energies are really disturbing to me. A friend of mine who is very psychic said to me when he used to walk down Camden Town, "It's like being psychically attacked by people." This is possibly their anger projected outwardly to other people as they pass.

All I really want to do is look out of the window, and eat sweet food. I suppose I have some eating disorder, and actually I am getting thinner even though I eat a lot, very "funnaaay."

Actually, I now understand why mad people laugh. Things do seem funny like when people stare at you, you feel like a film star or you see their own madness, by the expression on their faces. In the West End all these masses of people running hither and thither, the traffic roaring around, the noise, the fragmented gossip. If you suddenly stop dead still, and watch and listen, you realise you are in one big madhouse. It does strike one as being funny.

23 October

Writing a part of this novel? Last Monday about madness, I felt really good trying to concentrate. It made me focus my mind. I felt stronger, less fragmented. It felt good being creative and constructive, but the next day I felt really out of it.

I felt my mind disintegrating. I felt a sort of desolation, isolation, terrible fear socially. Nobody can help. I am lost in the void, trapped in my own dark pit.

I had to stop writing about going mad, just by writing about it, thinking about it, I was creating it. You suddenly slip into it through one's own imagination and fantasy, into the abyss.

There is a programme about London. It's called HOLDING ON. It seems so true. That's what London is about, TRYING TO HOLD ON.

Since writing the paragraphs above I had to have spiritual healing, because of my state of mind. I don't believe in sacrificing myself, self-martyrdom to achieve artistic creativity. I had "laying on of hands." It seems to have helped.

1998
Camden, London

Thoughts of a Lonely Man

4 March 1998

It's now March and I haven't written anything since last October. It's as if I have nothing to say. It all seems so pointless and yet I have a lot to say. It's just getting down to saying it or writing and concentrating. Why is it so hard to concentrate, to get one's mind together to be creative?

It's this feeling inside like this angst, or anxiety, this irritability, like something's not right. I feel something's going to happen. I need to be on guard, especially in the streets. Am I the only one who feels this, or is it just life, existence?

Do other living things have this dreadful feeling sometime that they have no right to exist anymore, or is it only human kind that have these thoughts? Or that they have existed too long and they shouldn't be here, shouldn't be alive.

It's time to go. There is no purpose, no point. I'm sure a psychologist would tell me what's wrong with me, or a priest, analysing me from their own perspective, of how a human being should be and act in the world, and live a useful life.

10 March

In fact I am doing all the right things and I still have these feelings. I do voluntary work in a community centre two mornings a week. I also help out in a drop-in centre for the mentally ill.

I think I SHOULD BECOME A MEMBER. I have started a men's group at the community centre. I have had therapy recently which I've now dropped.

It helps for a while. But it actually started to exhaust me so I stopped. It fragmented me even more. I do volunteer work in a hospital.

I have friends I can see if I want to. Nothing satisfies me. Maybe I expect too much from life, or think too much. Wayne, a friend in Brighton once told me that even when things were going well for me in Brighton, I wasn't happy. Somebody else said the same thing recently. They thought that I was a natural depressive.

Apparently according to psychologists most realists are depressives. They are realistic to the degree that they are aware that we are going to become ill and one day die and that life is full of pain, probably more emotional than physical these days.

I am supposed to be going to a talk tonight at the *Conway Hall*, Red Lion Square on "Self and the Cosmos (reflections on the life task)," given by a Quaker.

All afternoon I have been thinking, "Shall I go or not?" I can actually get a lift back if I want but its pouring with rain and very cold. I also have laryngitis and trying to get there by tube or bus is so exhausting. I have to decide in five minutes if I am going to go or not. ITS TOO LATE! I have got settled writing this nonsense and I can't stop. Later on I suppose I will regret not going. Why are decisions so difficult for me? Shall I go here or there? Shall I do this or that?

It's Easter Weekend now, Good Friday, and I haven't written anything since the beginning of March.

I have just read the last two sections of what I have written previously. It seems somewhat interesting about where I was at the time. Nothing has really changed, except that I have become obsessed with getting a computer to occupy my mind while alone in the flat to stop intrusive thoughts invading my mind. I have this urge to write, a sort of excitement that I must write, even though it's just to release frustration and to concentrate on concentration, not caring if what I write is good writing.

For years, when getting a thought about something I have been writing it down on a bit of paper with the idea of developing the idea later. But I rarely do so. I have all these bits of paper in a bag waiting for me to write about them. I had a clear out when I moved and chucked about a hundred bits of paper out. I have noticed they are mounting up again.

Sometimes if I look at the bits of paper I wonder what it was I meant to write about. I can't understand what I have written or why it seemed important at the time. I just manically write down things that come to my mind on this word processor.

28 July

I haven't written since Easter, as the reader can see. I am doing volunteer work in a community centre in Swiss Cottage. (That's an area in north London.) And it seems the centre is going the same way as the unemployed centre in Brighton, tearing itself apart because the Management Committee people have their own agendas within the committee and generally it's nothing to do with the centre's interest. It seems it's just to have a bit of power and try to influence and push their own bias on the decisions of management regardless of how it affects people. Mostly they don't read the reports or know what groups meet there or how the centre operates on a day to day basis.

I am beginning to get tired of it and feel I should move on. I have been there a year. Usually it's about a year in any one organisation and then I get tired and have to move on. It's very frustrating.

Actually I am very tired, exhausted really. It seems all the people I know are tired but busy. As long as they feel busy then it's okay. Everybody's busy and tired. They're so busy that they don't have time to feel tired because they're too busy. Their busyness in the end becomes manic, manically busy, manically tired. Aren't human beings strange?

5 August

I am becoming very visible in the streets again. People stare at me. This tends to last for a while. I think it's the strain on my face, a sort of intense expression, because I find being in the streets stressful after a while, or in a café or eating place. I sort of daren't look at people because as soon as I look they stare at me. A friend of mine in Brighton says she never looks at people. I find this very difficult, and yet at times if I look at people they won't look at me. I try and will them to look, and they will not look. It's like I am invisible. I find these two states of consciousness very bewildering and worrying.

6 August

Two days running I have written something. In these last ninety days I have written three times. It's like I have to do something I feel so bored with everything: bored, frustrated, indifferent and sad. Couldn't stop eating tonight even though I didn't really want the food.

Went for a walk on Primrose Hill because I felt so bloated. I did my best to avoid people on the Hill.

I suppose really I am lonely. The point is I know so many people and yet still feel cut off and isolated, like many people in this day and age. We are cut off from real communal belonging.

I am in pain. My ribs hurt when I breathe. I fell in the bath and cracked a rib. I heard it crack when I fell and the doctor said there is nothing he can do.

The pain will last about a month to six weeks. I can't sleep properly because of the pain and also at the back of my head, one of my sebaceous glands has got infected and has swollen up into a huge lump. The back of my head is very painful and pus is coming out of it. I found stains on my pillow this morning.

Once again, the doctor said he can't do anything, only give me antibiotics. They give these tablets out like sweets now and I must be immune to antibiotics, the amount I have taken. What a state to be in, ribs and head pain, dread going to bed tonight. I doubt if I will sleep. Another happy day gone by. How many more? This life will be the death of me.

Heard a saying today. Why can't people give others a piece of their heart instead of a piece of their mind? Thought it quite good.

11 October

I feel as if I am in some alien space or parallel world not connecting with people, and I want to write about it if I can because it is affecting the way people are reacting to me. I think it's suppressed anger, or it could be that I am trying to be present, to be here now, because my mind keeps slipping into some apathy or melancholia.

I don't hear what people are saying if I am listening to a talk, a TV programme or even friends talking around a table. When I am alone with somebody my attention span is feeble. Something has worried me this afternoon, which a lot of people probably wouldn't think too much about if they were in a café like I was in Belsize Park.

The waiters wouldn't serve me. It's not that they told me so, but because they ignored me for so long. It's because of the space I was in, the energy or expression that was on my face. When I arrived in the café, I was the next one to be served. There were waiters available. They were serving other tables but keeping a look out for other customers.

A couple came well after me two tables to my right and I knew the waiter would serve them first. He did. I thought shall I shout "Waiter!" or "Garcon!" or something out of frustration.

I decided to wait and see, out of curiosity. After what appeared to be a very long time the waiters were serving other people. I started to get nervous and embarrassed. I was waiting for a friend so I shifted to another table near the window but hoping the waiter would see me. After what seemed a long time the waiter finally came over from the serving bar with a look of irritability as though it was a great effort for him. I said I thought I was invisible. He didn't seem to understand. I think he was French or Italian, so I said, "Didn't you see me?" He never replied. Going back to the bar he spoke to another waiter and did the action of playing the violin. When he came back he never looked at me, just dumped the tea on the table. I nearly said, "I didn't know you could play the violin," but I didn't want to embarrass him.

Now just in case I was imagining this I observed what would happen when other people came in. My friend came in. The second he sat down the waiter came up to him. My friend even commented irritably, "I have only just come in."

The waiters continued to ignore me.

The thought crossed my mind that maybe it's because I look old. A couple of minutes later an older man came in and started to read a newspaper. Within a minute a waiter came up to him. I thought one of the reasons they had not approached me was because I had been reading a newspaper but they had interrupted the old man whilst he was reading.

I spoke to my friend about it and he thought it was possibly because I hadn't shaved as I am growing my beard again.

Another man came in who was about my age and looked like a writer, artist or musician. He had about a week's growth of beard and of course I had to watch. I suppose you will have now guessed that even as he sat down, they asked if they could help him.

As I was talking to my friend, concentrating on what he was saying, the waiters kept staring at me from the serving hatch. I wanted some hot water for my tea so I had to take courage and go up to the bar to ask for some, knowing that the waiters wouldn't want to notice me. When they gave me the water they never even looked at me.

The waiter who served my friend looked at him with concern and asked if he wanted anything else. My friend looked up, somewhat startled, and said, "No thank you." I said, out of pique, "I DO!" but the waiter never even looked at me and just walked away.

15 October

Something happened today that quite overwhelmed me.

I went to the community centre that I help out at, feeling I suppose a bit down. I had on this sweater with *Les Miserables* on the front, advertising the show. On the back was a picture of a young boy looking sad. I hoped nobody saw the words *Les Miserables*, because I suppose it reflected my mood.

I went into a room where there was a group meeting with older people. I know the facilitator there. I noticed a woman I knew talking to a volunteer who apparently was French. The show *Les Misrables* is, of course, based on a French story. We were just talking when she noticed my sweatshirt, "Oh!" she said. "*Les Miserables*! It suits you because you look so miserable."

I was taken aback. I suppose because I was feeling vulnerable. The woman I knew put her arm around me, I suppose to console me. The French woman said it again, three times, so I said I might look miserable but I feel OK and feel very aware of what's going on and I said some people act being happy and then the mask drops and you see the real person's character revealed. It might be angry, sad, indifferent etc.

Later on I felt irritation bubbling up in me. I walked over to the library, but couldn't concentrate so I walked back to confront her. Seeing her in the room I walked up to her and said, "Do you always speak your mind so readily to people you don't know?"

She said, "Yes. I'm French. I am an optimistic person, and I AM VERY POPULAR."

I said angrily, "It sounds like a put down to me."

She said, "I was only joking." I thought that saying three times the line "He looks so miserable," was not a joke. She then ignored me and started to talk to her friend. I said, "It seems insensitive to me." I don't know if she heard me or not and I then walked away.

In the office, I was talking to the woman who put her arm around me, so I spoke to her about it. She said, "She sounds very arrogant to say she's very popular." Looking round I saw in the other room that the French woman could see me talking in the office, so I looked at her and kept laughing as though I was having a good time talking to the woman in the office. I sort of exaggerated, overdoing it, and kept looking round at her. She shut the door.

The incredible thing was I started to feel this good feeling stirring in me, sort of giggly like a child who has done something mischievous. I felt happy as though I had dealt with something instead of walking away and not saying anything and feeling down. Previously I would carry the hurt around with me, possibly passing the hurt and anger on to somebody else.

I later heard from somebody else that she is quite often rude to people, and by confronting her it had helped me, because I had nipped it in the bud. And maybe she will think twice in the future about being rude to people? I believe it doesn't always help to turn the other cheek, in the Christian sense, because that hurt could be suppressed and explode onto somebody else, putting them down.

Later on in the afternoon I met my brother who I hadn't seen for six years. I was overwhelmed by him because of the story he told me. He had tried to commit suicide and was very lucky to be alive. We spoke for four hours, and I will try and write about it later.

25 October

Pouring with rain outside, going to rain all day, possible floods in Wales. Sat at my word processor. Thought I would try to write. Just sat there not even switching it on. Felt it was impossible because my mind couldn't focus. Felt too empty to concentrate. Put on TV. Watched an old rock and roll film, *The Girl Can't Help It*. All the old rockers were there, Little Richard, Gene Vincent, Eddie Cochran and others. Some I have never heard of, a few that were really good, a group called *The Chuckles*. Yes, *The Chuckles* were really good. Couldn't watch all the film, as per usual, switched it off, had a strong cup of coffee, plenty of sugar and felt the caffeine surge through my body into my brain. I felt the energy rising. My body responded by deciding to go to Baker Street Library to collect a book that I had ordered.

Sat in the reference library and became aware I wanted to write. I got a scrap of paper from the holdall bag, started manically to write this down. Can't seem to write about my brother's experiences yet. They seem too traumatic. It disables me.

3 November

I heard a talk on the radio about writers and how they write, and why they write, what they seemed to be saying and what they agreed on. They said, apparently with some pride, that they don't write about themselves. It's not the done thing, so where does that leave me, because all I do is write about myself. Thinking about this, I am sure they do write about themselves, but they are able to turn it into fiction.

Still can't write about my brother's experiences.

9 November

I saw my brother today and he started talking about when he was sectioned in a secure psychiatric unit after he tried to commit suicide. In the hospital he had to have someone with him for about a week twenty-four hours a day as he was on massive sedation and all he did was sleep.

For a month he couldn't go out of the grounds of the hospital, St Luke's, Muswell Hill. He was worried that he might never get out.

Apparently, from what he told me, he had been drinking heavily for weeks, and things started to come into his head that people were persecuting him and he started hearing voices sort of whispering and giggling. He thought people were accusing him of being a paedophile. He started to hallucinate. He never told me what the hallucinations were, but to escape the torment he decided to kill himself. He went to Tottenham Court Road Tube Station, went down to the platform and when the train came into the platform he jumped, but he slipped down in between the lines of the tracks and the train was over him. He was so determined to terminate his existence that he touched the electric live rail that was above him, but luckily for him that wasn't the electric rail. The electric rail was the one by the wall furthest from the platform.

In the police car or ambulance he thought the police were going to throw him out while the vehicle was moving, so he tried to get out when it was stopped at the traffic lights.

While in the hospital he tried to jump though the window. They had to inject him with something to put him OUT. There seems to be a genetic link here, because I don't know if I have mentioned it but our father committed suicide by jumping out of the third floor flat window in 1979 and my brother who had just gone into the room tried to grab him as he pushed himself out and actually had a hold of his leg but couldn't hold on to him.

He threw himself on the bed saying "He's gone, he's gone." That was the beginning of my brother's downhill struggle with madness.

15 November

I have a premonition, and I hope I am wrong, that I am ill. I have a lot of pain in my lower gut when I eat and I would not be surprised if I have something serious because of what I put in my stomach, because of emotional trauma over the years and more especially lately. For example, last week I ate half of an eight hundred gramme loaf in a day, plus about five bowls of cornflakes and other things during the day, completely out of control.

I feel compelled to do this sort of thing at least once or twice a week. I don't eat just white bread but other things, like chicken burgers or veggie burgers, at least two at a time, or more sometimes, just to fill this gap or empty feeling. I get messages from the past niggling at me that I am not okay. They are trying to undermine me like evil spirits or the devil sitting on my shoulder whispering in my ear.

In fact I think I have the Big C. I don't mind dying but I don't want too much pain. I am also wondering if I have somehow wished this on myself.

When I worked in the hospice I started to envy the people there, the patients that were dying. I wanted out. Life is too painful, too difficult. The society I knew I don't recognise anymore, but I can't explain what I mean, maybe another day, I might be able to put it into words, not today. I suddenly feel tired and sad so I'm going to stop writing.

21 November

The time has come, the Walrus said, to talk of many things and get our priorities right. I believe I have checkmated myself most of the time.

I find it difficult to breathe. My asthma is very bad and I put it down to the sort of heating I have, storage heating where the warm air is sent into the rooms distributing dust particles and house dust mites.

I even insisted that my landlord change my heater, so I could have one that you can put on when you like as well as storing heat over night. He agreed to my request and changed the heater, but the way the new heater is designed, it's worse for me. I was so pleased that I had got my way but it's turned out for the worse. I wish I had my old heater back. Life is such a gamble on the decisions we make.

Why I am a bit worried is that I am on oral steroids, something I have managed to avoid for a long time, as well as an inhaler steroid to get rid of the inflammation. These drugs are very bad for the immune system and they don't seem to be working that well, probably because I am being affected by the heating system and I hate being cold so I can't switch off the heating, unless I can think of an alternative to the heating system!

I am unable to go out because of the cold and my chest is bad, plus the crowds of people pushing and shoving and my own paranoia and anxiety about people in the streets. Also I am too anxious to go to the hospital about my stomach problem.

AND ANOTHER THING, I haven't seen hardly anybody for a week because I can't get out that much. I don't like inviting people around even when I can think of somebody to invite, because my flat is in such a mess.

Woe is me, checkmate thought? Maybe writing about all this might relieve some of the symptoms

(New Age thought). Maybe I am happy in misery, the famous words, WHY ME? And also WHY NOT ME? Decisions, decisions. (Love really is all you need.)

22 November

Collapse seems to creep up on one, but I don't really think it does.

The final collapse might happen suddenly, but it's the end of a cumulative process. People instinctively know they are damaging their health by their life-style, but they don't care. It seems a sort of death wish, pushing themselves to their limits, somehow justifying their martyrdom, and claiming they had no alternative.

Have spoken to only one person for about an hour in eight days. At the moment I don't feel that lonely. When I start feeling better I suppose all the fears and personal responsibilities will return. Going out into the streets mixing with people, socialising, paying bills, I wonder why we slip back into the old routine again. We don't seem to learn our lessons. It seems so difficult to do the things that are good for us. I will have to think of a way of keeping some of this peace that I have had these last eight days. What I do is slow down, do every thing as slow as possible, a sort of existentialist reality, possibly adding a spiritual dimension to life.

Funny thing is nobody phoned, except my brother. This is ironic, after all this time! For years I had to reject him because of his drinking and rage. Probably I did this at the time because I couldn't cope myself with my own stuff. That's my excuse.

I have the feeling I write out of compulsion, because it's irresistible. It's what I do to entertain myself, a phrase that Stefan, a Russian friend who I haven't seen for such a long time, used to say.

I play darts with myself. I am getting really good. I go round the board trying to get the trebles. It doesn't take long, I am amazed how often I get the treble. Practice I suppose. The only way to learn things is practice, creating a sort of positive habit. Funny how the brain starts to get familiar with a set pattern of things and doing, so I suppose, it's best to try, being as positive as possible. Thoughts of a hermit, an Urban Robinson Crusoe.

27 November

Well my asthma seems to be under control, hopefully it will stay that way. I am trying to eat sensibly, fruit and vegetables, less coffee, milk, tea and processed foods. I am trying to avoid stressing myself, if that is possible these days.

When I spoke about the Big C, it might be that I am becoming a hypochondriac. My stomach seems to have eased a little. I never went for the X-ray. All that stuff one has to drink that lights up your stomach, so they can see the X-ray, must be very toxic.

My illness has left me very weak, so I have to do things very slowly, which in a way is very peaceful, meditative even.

How do you make God laugh? TELL HIM YOUR PLANS. Seems an appropriate thing to say right now.

1 December

I was concerned about my perennial flowers in my window box, about six weeks ago because I thought they were dying, no buds and wilting. It was like it represented me. If they die I die. I was quite worried. Funny because I am not really a plant person, so I carefully took off the dead leaves and watered them. Now, the 1st of December, they have started to flower and bud, which is quite amazing because my flowers are practically the only ones on the block of twenty-four flats. Only two others have some sort of flowers. At first I thought this was a sign from Higher Forces that these plants are to help me by flowering, coming to life sort of thing. I thought mine must be the only ones on the estate that have flowered. I was disappointed when I realised that two others had flowers in their boxes. My consolation is that I don't really attend to the flowers like the others do.

Sometimes I have to be careful that I don't get into the idea that I am special, especially when you get into the spiritual stuff and live alone, and live a monastic life.

I go to monasteries to meet people who think like me so I realise I am not so special. It tends to ground me into everyday reality so that when I come home I'm more able to cope.

29 December

Unable to write for three weeks. Apathy. Mood swings from utter despair to "Oh well nothing really matters."

I went away for Christmas, five days in fact. I spent an

extra day because I couldn't face all the goodbyes to people. It was a Christmas gathering of Quakers. On the Sunday after Christmas I got out of the way while people were leaving. It's too emotional and sad. Not sure if I will go again. It's very difficult mixing with people if you are the sort of person who lives a monastic life.

Also it's very intense. Everybody's nice to each other, but there is a sort of unresolved tension when people are thrown together for five days, people who would not usually meet in the world outside and probably wouldn't get on with each other if they did meet.

When I phone people and ask "How are you?" invariably, (that's a good word) they say, "Fine, how are you?"

Generally I tell the truth. Usually it's not very positive, but it seems everybody's FINE, except me. WELL how come there is so much unhappiness, frustration, and anger around?

Seem to have survived my illness crisis that I had before Christmas. I am feeling stronger and more energised. It's what one does with the energy that's the problem.

I hope I can get on and do something creative this next year before the millenium.

I suppose at the end of 1999 we will say to each other see you in the next MILLENIUM!

1999
Camden, London

3 January

The hours are long.
THE DAYS ARE SHORT.

The days are long.
THE WEEKS ARE SHORT.

The weeks are long.
THE MONTHS ARE SHORT.

The months are long.
THE YEARS SHORT.

Time has gone.

OLD AGE.

Gerald, my recovering alcoholic brother, phoned just before Christmas, at 9.30 a.m. one morning demanding that I go to the hostel to see him. He sounded very angry and uptight. He said he had been drinking and felt depressed. I had just got out of the bath. I wasn't quite with it, as I had not been sleeping well and I was finding the mornings difficult. I was trying to get it together, to see when I could go to see him.

He snapped back at me, "JUST GOT OUT OF THE BATH! JUST GOT OUT OF THE BATH! Well get back in the fucking bath then!"

I said, "I don't think I will come and see you when you are in this frame of mind." He put the receiver down on me.

The thing is, Gerald is still living in the past, thinking I am going to run at his beck and call like my mother used to do for him. He also used to abuse her.

When she died I took over her role. For years he used to come up to my flat late at night, drunk. I had enough of it and had to tell him goodbye and to stand on his own two feet. I spoke to my mother about this when she was alive and asked her why she put up with it.

She said, "He's my son. You don't understand. You're not a mother." Well, she's right there. I don't understand.

Actually, he doesn't realise how lucky he is. The support he has at the hostel is very good. He has a social worker, a care worker and a psychiatrist to help him. I don't have any of this, only some inner strength and drive that prevents me going completely round the twist, SO FAR. I hope I can maintain it.

I have found it very difficult to write this tonight. I wanted to write about it just after it happened but ignored the feelings. I believe it would have been very cathartic for me because I have felt somewhat guilty about not going to see him. I will probably phone the careworker tomorrow to see how he is. Everything gets back to normal tomorrow regarding the Christmas break which finishes on the 4th January.

This is going to be the MOTHER OF ALL YEARS, this year, 1999, leading up to the year 2000. God help the earth and the people on it.

13 January

I spoke to a friend the other day. I suppose I do have some friends, even if the reverse seems more real most of the time.

He asked how I was. I said truthfully, "STRUGGLING." He replied, "Well, as long as you're STRUGGLING," which took me by surprise.

I heard a story which I think relates somewhat to all this. And I presume it's meant to be inspirational. It's about Jacob Epstein, the sculptor, who made a statue of a man embracing an angel. The story was of somebody wrestling all night with a figure and awoke in the morning with both of them exhausted. The man asked who the figure was but the figure refused to tell him but blessed him for struggling, then VANISHED!

14 January

Thirty economic advisors in the USA were wrong regarding 1998 including predictions on the stock market, unemployment and inflation.

Sovietologists in the Western World always used to try and explain what's going on in Communist Russia, but they never explained or predicted the downfall of Communism in 1989 and probably if they had tried they would have got it wrong because it was the problem of potatoes and soap and probably sink plugs that caused it. (Joke.) But these problems were real enough. They never have sink plugs in Russia. I have twice been to the Soviet Union and can confirm that these are genuine problems there. In the early building of the huge hotels catering for the western tourists, they made thousands of sink plugs but made them the wrong size. They never bothered to make new ones, so they did without them instead.

19 January

I'm a writer who cannot write. I want to write, but it seems impossible a lot of the time because of bodily weakness or stress and lack of concentration. I sometimes think I will write now and have a feeling of wanting to write, but feel hungry, so I have something to eat. I then find I don't want to write after eating.

I feel very apathetic about everything. All I want to do is sleep.

11 February

Dear diary this is the first entry for twenty-two days.

Well so many negative things have been happening to me it sometimes becomes laughable, all because of my state of mind which I can't seem to break free of. We, you, I, have to watch this. The mind is so powerful it can destroy one.

I had a course of steroids because my asthma became so bad and ever since then I have been unwell. I became bodily weak, got flu or something - funnily, something I don't usually get, probably because I don't mix with people, ha ha. I also got a stomach virus which has taken weeks to shake off. Slept for two days when I first had symptoms.

Last week I fell over and sprained my left elbow. I hope it's just a sprain, because I broke that elbow twice as a child and when they set it they set it wrong. I have always had a problem with it. It's dislocated but functionable. The doctors can't work out if it is the old dislocation, or a new one due to the recent fall. I have to go back to see them today.

In fact I have just had to stop typing with my left hand because my left elbow is aching. I am typing this with one finger. I am trying to invent a new me so I can break free of this pessimism.

Bought a new book called *Follow Your Heart*. Saw a woman reading it in a café and spoke to her briefly about it. It was on my mind for a week. Then one day I just went and bought it. It's very simple with a lot of funny meaningful illustrations.

There are a lot of things happening on the Social Benefits front which are making people very anxious. They're trying to make people work including one-parent families and disabled people who obviously are unable to work. Asylum seekers will not get any money, only food vouchers. I have a huge incapacity benefits questionnaire that I have to fill in. If I don't get it right I will lose benefits. It's the means test all over again.

"Must remain positive, oh yes, oh yes, hmm, hmm, don't be

cynical, Crusoe. Everything will be okay.
    HELP!"

15 February

God I feel so frustrated and angry with everything, with myself, society, the media, people, politics, my writing. I'm SO pessimistic.

Pessimism is a part of me, a part of my structure no matter how much I think I have put it down, and this self-obsession is driving me to insanity. My narcissism is causing me to have a life romance with my self, but I don't fancy me. I don't even like me. Fancy having a romance with a person you don't like. Must be a form of hell. Maybe that's what insanity is.

18 February

This pessimism has at times led me into a sort of fantasy that I am Sydney Carlton, a drunk and the main character of Charles Dickens' book, *A Tale of Two Cities*. He takes the place of a man who is going to be executed because he feels worthless and is in love with the woman who this man is going to marry, even though she doesn't return his love. She doesn't know he loves her, but possibly has an inkling, like all women do about men.

But she will find out about him after he's dead.

While on the scaffold he says, "Who would weep for me, who would weep for a life lived, a worthless life?"

NOBODY. But somebody will weep for ME now. IT'S A FAR, FAR BETTER THING I DO NOW THAN I HAVE EVER DONE and a far, far better rest I go to.

My morbid sentimentality!

20 February

I bought a bottle of Bacardi a few months ago. Last night I thought I would have a couple of glasses. I thought it might make me break free of this apathy. I fell asleep and when I awoke I felt ravishing hungry and couldn't stop eating.

I remember listening to a talk on drink on the radio by a doctor. He said alcohol destroys vitamins and minerals and that's why people become hungry and if you have a hangover the next morning you should have a big breakfast (a big fry up if you can face it) to replace the vitamins and minerals that you have lost.

27 February

Read an entry in a *Faber Book of Diaries* by a woman of the Bloomsbury set. She was a friend of most of the set and worked in a bookshop that was the mainstay of the group in Bloomsbury. The article she wrote seemed to be saying something to me. It goes:

4 May 1948

I quite often look back at the pleasures and pain of youth, love, jealousy, recklessness and vanity - without forgetting their spell, but no longer desiring them; while middle-aged ones like music, places, botany, conversation seem to be just as enjoyable as those wilder ones, in which there was usually some potential anguish lying in wait, like a BEE in a flower.

I hope there may be further surprises in store and on the whole do not fear the advance into old age.

On Thursday I must have had one of my manic days. I seem to have done so much. In the morning I went to a bible study class for about an hour and a half.

Later on I went to a community centre to play bingo with old age pensioners. I started to feel uneasy there - only played one session and had to get out. They asked "Only playing one?" I pretended I had a doctor's appointment.

After that I went to a meeting on mental health for about two hours regarding changes going on in Camden Social Services. Felt I didn't belong to any of the three groups. I was an outsider, an observer of it all. Felt very isolated when I came home. It was dark and very miserable and the night seemed full of foreboding.

Yesterday I didn't do anything. I just slept and ate.

6 March

I feel very anxious and manic. Just came in from the streets from shopping, put on a tape of Gregorian chant to try and calm down. My friend Peter, who had a heart attack a few months ago, said to me, "Take it easy. Don't have a heart attack like me." The funny thing is, a few days earlier, I felt I had better calm down as I am having a lot of funny pains in my chest. When these synchronizing things happen, they tend to worry me. Been going to pubs lately and drinking a glass of house wine.

One night I had this fantasy that I was Herman Hesse's Steppenwolf from a book of the same name. He used to go in taverns in Germany before the Second World War and order a bottle of wine and drink all night, too lonely to go back to his flat. Just to sit in the tavern and reflect on his alienation like a wolf of the steppes observing, watching and slinking out unseen and unobserved.

I have recently had this feeling of being invisible again, and sometimes the opposite feeling of being too visible and feeling paranoid, and not wanting people to look at me when they actually do and wanting them to notice me when they don't. Possibly the result of my body language, oh I don't know. Illusion surrounds us all.

10 March

My word processor is on the blink. I can't print out any writing that I have typed . It's going to cost me a lot of money to repair it at least half of what the machine cost. I have to get a new one or a PC instead. They cost a lot of money and it's

making me anxious about deciding which I need to continue.
BLOODY NUISANCE!

12 March

I am writing on this disc not knowing if I can retrieve what
I write. I have been told I could under special circumstances at
a computer shop I visited. I would have to pay for this to be
done.

General every day computers wont take this word processor disc. I am very undecided what to do about the situation.
This is putting it very mildly. I am in high anxiety about the
whole problem. I am amazed how one can get so fearful about
what to do. Is it because of my childhood rejection by my
mother and father? A part of me is looking at it with amusement and disbelief and another saying, "Make a decision and
pull yourself together." The amusement part is probably a
form of mild hysteria.

I have just thought of Les Dawson, the comedian, saying
"She's having a hystericalectomy," instead of a HYSTEREC-
TOMY, ha, ha.

I might put down tomorrow what my options are. There are
three it seems. Oh blow it I will do it now.

The first option is supposedly the best one. I can buy a PC
for £400 second hand, with a printer.

Second option, get this word processor repaired at a cost
£95 when it only cost £200 to start with.

Thirdly, I could buy a computer from a friend for £190.
The last one I probably won't do for reasons which I don't want
to go into. She seems very uptight lately, that's all I am going
to say. I keep thinking about my friend's offer, but keep
changing my mind. I don't want to spend £400 on one. In fact
I wouldn't want to spend £400 on anything it's so much
money.

30 March

After three weeks of high anxiety and near hysteria, so
much suffering for nothing it seems, I have decided to get this

word processor repaired. The engineer is coming tomorrow. It's like a huge weight off my mind and it feels so good to be able to write once again. It's like I never realised how good it feels. I took it all for granted before. It's like a big release from a heavy burden, a sort of ecstasy.

I hope I am not taking this analogy too far.

God, I have so much to say but don't know where to start. That word God seems so relevant. A part of me would like to finish this manuscript and say I am going to seek God and drop out of Society and lead a contemplative life. I have said this before and will probably say it again. A monastery would be nice and quiet for a while.

31 March

My birthday. Received three cards. Fifty-eight years in this incarnation. What have I learnt? Not much! No more to say.

2 April

Good Friday. "They rejected him. They despised him. They esteemed him not." Old Testament, Isaiah 54. God bless all the Jesuses in the world. You can see why the beggars, mentally deranged, and down and outs can identify with Jesus.

8 April

I have been reading a book on psychosis and creativity. I think it's probably true that psychosis is helpful to creativity if you are trying to create something that hasn't been done before. If you have it though, it's very stressful.

I came back on the 6th April from Brighton. I spent three days there, staying with a friend of mine, Sheila Smith.

She is quite famous in Brighton being on Radio Brighton many times and performing at the Festival every year, a seventy-year-old who has the energy of a fifty-year-old, and an even younger spirit. She teaches Egyptian dancing which is very sophisticated. People think it's just belly dancing but it's not.

Even I like it. Over the years the music has grown on me. When I first heard it in the 1980s I couldn't stand it - the wailing and up and down melody! But now I listen with "sweet surrender." Maybe that's a bit over the top.

Coming back to London after being in Brighton for three days I felt really isolated, and wondered why I ever left. I think, probably, I have evolved somehow and would now be able to tolerate the Brighton I described earlier.

This isolation made me very manic when I got back. Anything to escape the feelings of loneliness and void in someway helped me because it made me mix with people I generally wouldn't mix with.

In the bath about half hour ago I had so much to say about what I wanted to write about. Now I can't remember what it was. Oh yes, I took my manuscript to Brighton to write something more, but was unable to because of the excitement of being there. I told Sheila about what I had written. She wanted to read it and afterwards said she couldn't put it down and read the whole thing that evening and blamed my manuscript for making her forget to use her asthma inhaler that night. I felt really good about her comments because I was becoming disillusioned with the whole thing. We all need positive feedback. Somehow it creates optimism. We're just like children even at our age. Aren't we strange, us humans?

Meeting my brother today. He wants to take my photograph. Why, I don't know.

10 April

I want to conclude this manuscript on Mr Robinson Crusoe, wandering around the Urban asylum, meeting ships in the night or mostly in the day, fellow travellers on this planet called earth. They, like me, wondering what they're doing here, and also a lot of them who have left as one day will I, but not till I have finished this bloody manuscript.

Where to? That's the question. A parallel world maybe, or a different dimension. This is the current vogue of thought. Or to be reincarnated back here. What a thought, to have to go through all this again, or be resurrected. I can't get my head round that one.

Anyway, back to today's reality. It's suddenly gone cold and heavy. I don't want to go out. I have to get some shopping. Feeling very apathetic and isolated.

12 April

A friend suggested I should take this logbook into the year 2000. I don't think I have the stamina or that my nerves can stand it.

Spending those three days with Sheila in Brighton, and being isolated in London, has left me feeling very anxious and alone. I have this terrible feeling of dread, and feel like the painting *Scream*, by the artist Munch. The figure in the painting has his mouth wide open, and a haunted look on the face. They had this image on the London underground a little while ago.

I have had to stop smoking because my chest and throat seem like the back end of a grate. Also a glass of wine doesn't seem to agree with me. This leaves me with virtually no props to prop me up, and I feel awful, sort of dead. "DEAD MAN WALKING," as they call out in the penitentiaries in America when they execute somebody and he is walking to the execution chamber.

21 April

I went away again last weekend, with a friend to a college reunion of his. This is the second time I have been with him. I enjoyed it, but coming back to London again and adjusting to a sort of completely different way of existing is starting to undermine me. I am not going to go away again for a long time. The adjustment is too difficult when I return.

I have so much to say but seem unable to get it out and I feel very stressed and frustrated with everything. All I see is anger and stress, which probably says where I am coming from.

All I want is peace and I can't seem to get it. External events affect one, never mind how much I try to avoid it. The social disintegration, the war in the Balkans, the million people forced out of their country in Kosovo. Nostradamus's predictions seem to be fated to be worked out from the 1990s to the year 2000.

I noticed in the Catholic school and Covent opposite where I live, a banner celebrating the "2000 AD Jubilee." Never thought of it as a jubilee!

Pessimistic thought, but reality - two students in America on a college campus killed fifteen other teenage students because the killers felt they didn't fit in. They killed the students because they hated them and then killed themselves. Obviously they also hated themselves just as they did the others.

The mind boggles when things like that happen.

Jill Dando, the TV presenter, killed. Nobody seems to know why. More anger.

23 April

After being away then coming back to London and getting on a bus the other day, I sort of ran for the bus and just managed to get on. The bus driver never even looked at my bus pass, and started to drive off when I wasn't really on the bus. I let that go but I said, talking to the passengers, turning round to them, because I sat near the top end of the bus, "You can get on the bus for free these days. They don't bother to look at your pass."

Nobody looked at me. Nobody agreed. Nobody acknowledged me. They all sat staring straight ahead, like zombies on a day out. One man glanced at me out of the corner of his eye.

I tried to attract his attention, or get some response from him. He quickly looked away.

I looked around two or three times. They all sat transfixed, eyes staring into space like mad people in a catatonic state, just sitting there, deadly quiet. So I said out loud, "Bloody hell! I'm back in London! Back in the madhouse!" hoping somebody would comment. Still no response. It made me nervous, so I started to giggle. It then dawned on me: they now think I am the mad one sitting here giggling to myself.

I would like to end this journal on a positive and objective note but I am unable to do that right now. Anyway, all this subjective, and introspective attitude is a dangerous way to exist. Enough is enough.

I would like to live a contemplative life within a religious community or even a monastery - if I could believe and have faith in the doctrine. I would like to go back to the melancholy and mystical world I used to be in, away from the samsara illusion of the secular world.

25 April

I have realised why a lot of people are stressed. I blame a lot of the problem on the government. They have this policy, recently, of challenging everyone's settled existence. For example, they are having people assessed, people on the following benefits: unemployment, incapacity, and disability. Local councillors, school teachers, doctors are also implementing so many changes to the social services that people can't keep up with it all - neither the implementers nor the users who are all trying to understand the changes. Many of the changes are not necessarily for the better. In any case, they create anxiety and confusion. It's bureaucracy gone mad - all to save money, and yet they can always find enough money for war, always costing BILLIONS, and many lives - as in the Falklands, the Gulf, the Balkans, Kosovo, and others to come?

4 May

I wonder if a lot of people decide to go spiritual because of feeling socially inadequate. It does tend to help. It feels sort of free, more peaceful. You don't have the pressure of having to form intimate relationships. It's just you and God. Mind you, I suppose a lot of spiritual people would disagree with what I have just said, especially Christians. They would say the reverse: that it's relationships that matter. But for those who feel socially inadequate it's a way out of the rat race and if it gives one peace, why not?

Gerald, my younger brother started drinking again. I went to see him at the hostel. It was a very hot day. He had the curtains drawn and said people could see him across the road so he kept his window shut. His room was stifling. He was very paranoid and was worried that the hostel management were going to chuck him out.

He kept going on about a contract he had signed agreeing not to drink while at the hostel. I think it was guilt that was causing him to suffer. He has always felt socially inadequate.

I also found out he attempted suicide again at Camden Town Tube Station after Christmas. He jumped on the line again or got down on to it. It was on a newspaper poster: "MAN ON LINE AT CAMDEN TOWN UNDERGROUND" or something like that.

I actually vaguely remember this and, not realising it was him again, thought of Gerald two years previously when he had jumped at Tottenham Court Tube. He really is lucky to be here.

5 May

Why am I writing this journal? Why did RC write his log book? I suppose to keep a record until he was rescued. Who is going to rescue me? Am I more free than before, after five years of writing this journal? I think I might be, but is one really ever free of internal emotions? Probably not until one expires. Even then, if reincarnation is true, you might not be free because you take your stuff with you to the next life. If it's true you can't escape, isn't it best to deal with it now?

I suppose it's how one can be with the feelings and not be overwhelmed by them, because they are just feelings and thoughts. Maybe it's about choosing which feelings and thoughts we can have, to create options, about feeling better, to be more free of negative thoughts. Blimey, I am going on again!

10 September

I feel dried up with nothing more to say. I feel I've written it all out of me. I want to just become a drifter, one of the crowd waiting for the millennium with unease. And watching TV, eating all the wrong foods, getting panicky, withdrawing, and having no energy.

One thing I did recently though, was to appear on the radio programme, *All in the Mind* with Dr Anthony Clare, talking about schizophrenia. Something I know about even though I am not schizophrenic. My problem is more one of having a mood swing scenario. I was discussing a book that a friend of mine, Dr Peter Chadwick, wrote. The book is called, *Schizophrenia, the Positive Perspective*. I am featured in a whole chapter. I did it and went along with it because I wanted throughout my life always to have my say about reality, meaning, and the society we live in.

What I feel has made me start writing again is reading a book called *Camden Parasites* which I will explain later, because my concentration is waning already.

15 September

I was in Brighton last week in the Pavilion gardens talking about this book *Camden Parasites* by Daniel Wright, alias Daniel Lux. This word Lux is very interesting. I looked it up in the dictionary to see why he chose this name. It means a unit of illumination. I think that is how he saw himself, light in the dark of the Camden underground scene.

Anyway, back to Brighton. I was with Wayne, a friend I mentioned earlier in the book, talking about this book I had read, *Camden Parasites*. Out of my eye I saw what looked like a drunk or drug addict coming into the Pavilion gardens. Out of all the people in the Gardens he came up to me within seconds of me talking about this drug addict in Camden and started a conversation with me. He actually made me quite nervous. He seemed in an angry mood, and as Wayne had his child with him we decided to move on. I pointed out that we had been talking about a drug addict when he moved in on me. Wayne seemed to agree there was some synchronicity there.

Back to the book. I couldn't put *Camden Parasites* down because I know most of the places in Camden that he wrote about. I love his narrative about his discussions with his friends, something I find difficult to put into writing. When I saw his picture in the *Camden Journal* I thought I recognised him from somewhere, probably it was Inverness Street where he had his stall.

He lived on and off the streets of Camden, staying with friends and lovers, some of them well off. I find the streets difficult and dangerous, and generally keep away if I can help it and keep to myself, two different realities of Camden.

24 September

Carrying on from my last entry about Daniel Wright (alias Danny Lux) and *the Camden Parasites* book . . . What gets me high and I only really came across this yesterday . . .

I was feeling very flat like my brain was thick with mush, and I was dragging my body around like it was weighed down with heavy chains, something like out of Charles Dickens' story, *A Christmas Carol*. Marley's ghost, who haunted Ebenezer Scrooge, with such chains dragging behind him it looked horrendous . . . but I digress.

So I went into the *O2 Centre* in Finchley Road where they have a huge area consisting of cinemas, children's disco, restaurants, huge fish tanks with tropical fish, and a supermarket, and then, adding a surreal atmosphere, palm trees and fountains that squirt water along the side of the elevator as you pass. Again I digress.

I went into the coffee bar of *Books Etc.* which is a huge bookshop that people go into and read books just like a library with large settees that they sit on. People sit there all day and read without buying a book. I don't know how they make it pay.

Anyway, I ordered a medium coffee which actually is very large, bigger than a mug of coffee. On the side of the counter they have chocolate that people put in their cappuccino, so I put chocolate into my coffee, sat down to drink it. Then I went back because I felt I needed more chocolate, sat down, and slowly well quite quickly really, started to become aware of my surroundings and myself, sort of awoke from apathy, felt energised and concentrated. I was able to do my shopping and also went to a discussion that evening on therapeutic communities, something I wasn't going to go to because I felt so flat and rough. I was amazed by the effect that chocolate and coffee had on me. I think without the chocolate the effect is much less. That's how sensitive I am to chemicals, and it's enough for me.

It amazes me that Danny Lux put so much chemicals in himself and lived so long, but I can understand the high from just having chocolate and coffee.

27 September

I have been staying in Lewes, a town in Sussex not so far from Brighton. I commute there from London spending half a week in London and the other part in Lewes, staying with a German friend, Ivo, who I have mentioned earlier in the book. He is a musician and healer, although he doesn't give healing to me, but it's good to stay with him a part of the week.

The other day I saw a man I knew in the 1980s. He lived rough and some of the time he slept in St James's Church Piccadilly, in the basement where the boiler was, and also he used a garden shed in the small gardens there, and had a cassette player and a bed cum bench, small heater and light. I think he had a small fridge. We used to go and talk to him some of us who used the church for alternative events and lectures.

His name was Terry. He was very tall with short dread-locks. We used to talk about philosophy and spiritual matters. He seemed very knowledgeable and also with his street aware-ness very practical in the survival sense.

When I go to St James's, which is very rarely now, I think about him. I wonder if he is still alive. The mortality rate for people on the street is very high, but I think one of the big reasons for this is drink and drugs.

Terry once told me, and I must admit when he pointed it out I could tell it was true, that he never washed. He said the reason he never smelt was because he didn't drink, and he put out his bare arm for me to smell and it was true he didn't smell. He said his clothes smelt if he wore them for too long but he just changed them and threw the old clothes away.

Anyway, approaching Charing Cross Station last Thursday I saw him leaning against a lamp post eating a small carton of yogurt with his finger scraping around the edge and putting it in his mouth. He looked well, in fact looked very well. I shouted "TERRY!" He never even looked up so I went up to him and said, "TERRY, do you remember me? It's DES." He just shook his head. I said, "No? Don't you remember me?"

He just shook his head again, without looking at me. I walked away feeling disconsolate.

29 September

I try to be positive. To me being positive means having a spiritual meaning to life. I think of life as an adventure, with the good, the bad and the ugly. I have a sort of curiosity about it all, so I wonder what will happen to me, and how much am I in charge of my life. How much power do I have to change it to make it better and to help others on the way if am able? Do I create my own reality? Can I become more free? I don't know but maybe it's worth a try.

30 September

I seem to be writing every day these last few days, maybe trying to get it all out. After writing yesterday's paragraph, I came across this card in my bag which I had been carrying around with me for months. It's called *Vision* by Joy Cowley.

Two people watched the same sunset.
One said, "At times like this I am afraid.
The sky is so vast, the sea is so immense.
In comparison, I'm a speck of dust,
here today, gone tomorrow.
When I look at the hugeness of creation,
I feel my insignificance
and I wonder what my life is all about."

The second person said,
"What a glorious sunset, just think!
I am the reason that this exists.
I am the only proof I have of all the beauty in this world.
Without the gift of my life, the gift of my senses,
all this would be as nothing.
I praise God that the universe is held
in the wonder of my Being.

May the force be with you. Whither will I wander? A FAR FAR BETTER THING I DO NOW THAN I HAVE EVER DONE.

Divine Uniqueness

Everybody is unique.
There has never been anybody like you before
And there never will be again.

In that uniqueness, in that individuality
There is no comparison with anything else,
With no other entity, no other being.

In that sense, that being must be perfect,
Perfect in its own right
In its own creation.

If that being is perfect
In its own right,
It must also be beautiful.

If that being is perfect and beautiful
In its own right,
Then it must also be divine.

If that being is perfect and beautiful and divine
In its own right,
Then it must also have the light within,
A spiritual light.

So, perfect and beautiful and divine-lighted spirit,
What's it like to be human?!

1990

2001
Camden, London

24 July

I need to try and write about love, not the love of *California Dreaming* or the naff soppy stuff or even romantic love, but the power of the Vibes.

According to Victor Frankl, one of the greatest psychotherapists of the post Second World War era, the most important meaning anyone can have in their life is love.

I am in the staff cafeteria in the Royal Free Hospital. The public can use it, but we pay extra. For what you are offered it's still very reasonable and cheaper than greasy spoon type caffs. The people that frequent this place, aside from the staff, and generally in the evenings, are, shall we say, like me. They are a bit eccentric and restless, or like Dostoyevsky's underground man.

Anyway I got sidetracked from the subject of love. The Beatles, thirty odd years ago wrote a song, *All You need Is Love*. John Lennon wrote, "I write and talk about love because I am a violent man."

I'm not a violent man but an angry and melancholic man. I suppose that's the kindest thing I can say about myself. I'm writing about love because most of the time I don't have it either for myself or for others. What this does is make one feel at times isolated, lonely and fearful, especially in the city.

When I am with nature I feel relaxed and renewed even after a short period especially in woods.

I know a lot of people and in fact had seventeen Christmas cards, but spent Christmas alone. It's a regular occurrence which always puzzles me.

When I am in a more positive or loving mood, I can't say that it's very often, these feelings I'm not saying they disappear, but they seem less of a problem.

Why I find it so hard to love could be something to do with early childhood when I was rejected by my mother. I believe this created inner rage, and hopelessness. Possibly and probably that's what a psychologist would say, like my friend, Dr Peter Chadwick, who wrote about me in two of his books* explaining why he considers me a schizotypal person and at the same time calls me a mystic.

Well it seems to me there are probably millions of people who are labelled mentally sick in the cities of Great Britain who are actually not really sick, who if in India would be called mystics. That may be one reason why there are apparently less mentally ill people in proportion to the population in India than in Great Britain.

But love as a power! Now there's a thing, being in a state of love is apparently supposed to be good for your well-being. That means it is good for your immune system. You experience less stress, less illness, less fear, less loneliness, less isolation and probably helps you to have more friends, and more freedom.

Well that's the theory, but I don't know about those last two. All I know is I can't take too much of it. It starts to undermine me, and makes me nervous. It starts to irritate me. The feelings of being isolated and cut off seem more familiar and safer for me, and it's not just me.

It could be that this is the problem for people who can't love. It feels safest to be experiencing the absence of love. This is the opposite to the idea of the book written years ago called *Women Who Love Too Much*. There is a line from

* See Peter Chadwick's books, *Personality as Art*, chapter 6, and *Schizophrenia, the Positive Perspective*, chapter 6.

William Blake that says, "We are put on earth for a little space that we may learn to bear the beams of love." The emphasis to me is on the word LEARN. So we have to learn to love. So there are millions out there in the cities and towns who have never learnt to love. It seems to make sense. Very young children generally only want to have their needs met, be it food or toys, until they start to get older and have to learn to consider others.

I was in the doctor's surgery the other day when this woman came in with two children in her arms. One was I suppose about two months the other about two years old. The very young baby was looking around with big dark eyes trying I suppose to make sense of the world around it and suddenly it would focus on a person for a long period of time. I always wonder what they see, maybe light or dark energies in that person? The older one was cuddling the mother, sort of trying to hide his face in her breast but quite restless and looking around while the mother was trying to calm him. Then a Chinese lady with her child came in. The mother, after sitting down, tried to interest the child with a Meccano type toy on the floor. I was lost with involuntary absorbing interest at these two mothers. The mother with the two children gave me a half smile. Suddenly I realised that what I was looking at was love, the mothers' love for their children, unconditional love. I know it's an everyday occurrence but it can be quite startling when it confronts you. I started to feel sad and uncomfortable as I realised that all those feelings back when I was a child had never been resolved with my mother. I was glad when my name was called to see the doctor.

I suppose many people don't allow themselves to love because there are a lot of things at risk: pain from the past and fear of the future, when actually there is only the present.

There is a paragraph from Paul Coelho's book, *Veronika Decides to Die*. I won't put it in context as it's too complicated. The paragraph goes like this:

Before you say again that you're going to die I want to tell you something. There are people who spend their entire life searching for a moment like the one you had last night, but they never achieve it. That's why if you were to die now, you would die with love in your heart.

I frequent, as I said before, the *02 Centre* on Finchley Road and have coffee at *Books Etc*. They know me there as well as the other regulars. A lot of underground people go there. Like the Royal Free Hospital cafeteria, it's a sort of meeting place. People take books off the shelves and read while they're having coffee, sometimes even buying them.

I was talking to a born again Christain one day at *Books Etc*. I won't mention her name because she might read this. She was a white African, tall, dark, very attractive. She seemed in a depressed mood and started revealing to me her problems about her relationship with her friends and started crying. I was perplexed about what to do, so I tried to comfort her the best I could. After a while she said she felt better, and commented that she thought I was a loving person. I was surprised by this remark and said I suppose so, but I have to work very hard at it. I was feeling empathic that day. Mind you, she was very attractive so it was easier to feel that way towards such a person.

I think the idea of being attractive may be important. If a homeless person on the streets who is, let's say, not a very attractive human being, even possibly ugly, and is rejected day after day, and even has violence done to him and through it all is able to love or be empathic towards others I would put this person on a par with a SAINT.

It seems much harder to love in this day and age. People seem to have no time, especially in cities - fast living, fast food, faster computers, information overload. We absorb more information in one day than Renaissance man did in his whole lifetime. One in four people live alone compared to one in twenty thirty years ago. There's isolation, lack of trust, single parents. A large majority of kids are out of control on estates. There's negative news on the TV and radio from around the world right into your front room. There's no wonder depression, drugs, and alcohol abuse are on the increase.

If we can't get love from a society that's sick, then we must get it for ourselves in our own individuality and uniqueness. Without love, life is meaningless. Once you have love within you, never mind how small, life becomes more meaningful.

So to all the people I meet at the Royal Free Hospital cafeteria, and *Books Etc* at the *02 Centre*, Finchley Road: poetess and fiction writer, Oshunah, named after the goddess Oshun, who is the Yoruba goddess of unconditional love, Greek Bob, who must have read most of the books at *Books Etc* on computers and new age theology, polite and charming Jake, otherwise known as Mithras, who always looks for the good in people, Malcolm who once walked across the Sahara desert alone or at least to the middle and back, beautiful biblical Kath, chairman Yash, another mystic and crossword addict, darting Dougan, who is here there and everywhere, Harvey, mathematics teacher, who belongs to about thirty different societies and comes out with his own sayings called Harveyisms, Steven who could have been a top class athletics runner who once ran with Gordon Pirie, a famous miler in the fifties, Ovid, who has an economics degree with distinction, and to people from the New Directions Camden drop-in centre - Lou, bacteriologist, user-rep and computer whizz, Irish Sean, ex-university chappie and pool table master, Giles, Rumpole of the Bailey, ex-lawyer, and Loretta, ex-schoolteacher who still thinks she is one, and my brother G - to all these people, who do not exist on the remote corners of humanity but are on a par with the great and famous and at the centre of it and civilisation with their imaginations and obsessions, the basis of every inventive, creative, persevering and scientific thought, * and without whom, and people like them, we would still be in the dark ages - I send my love and my esteem - to you all, and all the underground people who wander the windswept dirty cities of Britain.

* Some people who have suffered from depression, or paranoia, or exhibited schizoid or schizotypal traits

Spike Milligan, English comedian.
Chiang Kai-Shek, statesman, Chinese leader.
Isaac Newton, English scientist and mathematician.
Abraham Lincoln, President of USA.
Winston Churchill, English Prime Minister and writer.
Cardinal Newman, English prelate and theologian.
Rod Steiger, American actor.
Igor Stravinsky, Russian composer.
Jacob Epstein, British sculptor of Russian-Polish-Jewish descent.
Hermann Hesse, German writer.
Victor Hugo, French writer.
Somerset Maugham, English writer.
John Wesley, English founder of Methodism (a large British Protestant Christian sect).
G.B.Shaw, Irish writer.
W.H. Auden, Anglo-American writer.
Maurice Ravel, French composer.
Albert Einstein, German-Swiss-American scientist.
Gustav Mahler, Austrian composer.
Van Gogh, Dutch artist.
Sigmund Freud, Austrian founder of psychoanalysis.
Carl Gustav Jung, Swiss psychiatrist and thinker.
Ludwig Wittgenstein, Austrian-British philosopher and mathematician.

Postscript

After Urban Robinson Crusoe left the café in Hampstead I noticed that he had left on the table a single sheet of paper, folded and slightly grubby, as if it had been at the bottom of a bag for a long time. I opened it and read the title, *ONLY ONE TRUTH*. I still wonder if he left the paper there on purpose or just mislaid it when he gave me the journal.

ONLY ONE TRUTH

I come across many Christians who think theirs is the only true religion. There are apparently about seventy religions in the world, and if one of these religions is the real truth, all the other paths - sixty-nine of them - must be untrue. And yet possibly the real essence of each one, if it comes from the heart and has the fundamental principle of unconditional love, must also be the truth.

How can we really know the absolute truth? Just being a part of matter distorts our perception, our sense of what the real truth is, and we feel separate in our pain, with all its fears, bias, hurts, resentments, anger. The separateness that we feel is the forgetting of who we really are: beings of light who just happen to be in matter, in the human form.

Neither Christianity nor any other religion can claim that it is the only true way. And do we really believe that it makes any difference to God whether we make the sign of the cross, pray towards Mecca three times a day, or wear a kippa on our head? The only thing we can be sure of is unconditional love, the universal law, which we may have a glimpse of now and then.

> "There is only one religion, the religion of love.
> There is only one caste, the caste of humanity.
> There is only one God, the omnipresent God.
> There is only one language, the language of the heart."

Sri Sai Baba

What we need today is not a new society, not a new education, not a new religion, but individuals with purity of mind and hearts to heal the deep wounds, conflicts and misconceptions of our country and our world. I don't see the Resurrection in the Christian sense, as being in a different dimension, but the Resurrection as a change in consciousness on this planet.

Also published by Saxon Books

Minds at War
The Poetry and Experience of the First World War
Edited by David Roberts

Minds at War is the largest anthology of poetry of the First World War and it has a wealth of background information too. It has 50 per cent more poems than the Penguin Anthology of First World War Poetry (250 poems in all).

The poetry
- The selection concentrates on the classic poems by the greatest poets of the war
- Women poets are exceptionally well represented
- There are examples of the once hugely popular poems which were written as propaganda.

Important background
Historical and biographical background material, including extracts from diaries, and personal letters of poets, and comments from pundits, politicians, and newspapers help to provide the necessary context and deepen our understanding of both the poetry and the psychological landscape of the war.

More information on www.warpoetry.co.uk

9"x6" Paperback Illustrated Third Printing

410 pages   ISBN 0 952 8969 0 7   £13-99 (UK)

Also published by Saxon Books

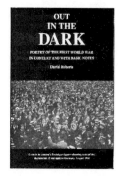

Out in the Dark
Poetry of the First World War in Context and with Basic Notes
Edited by David Roberts

For students and the general reader
This anthology, based on **Minds at War**, has been prepared for the general reader who requires less background information than there is in **Minds at War**, and for students, including GCSE and A level, who need to understand the contexts of poems.
Out in the Dark contains:
- the great classic poems of the First World War
- a wide range of popular and propagandist verse
- a substantial selection of poems by women writers
- basic notes on almost all poems (140 in total)
- ample material for in-depth course work studies
- important historical and biographical information
- Comments of past and present day critics give starting points for considering "alternative interpretations" of many poems

"The best war poetry anthology for students."

More information on www.warpoetry.co.uk

9"x6" Paperback, Illustrated, Second Printing

192 pages   ISBN 0 952 8969 1 5   £7-99 (UK)

Also published by Saxon Books

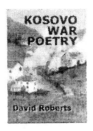

KOSOVO WAR POETRY AND VERSE
by David Roberts

An Englishman, whose earliest memories are of German bombers overhead, considers the bombing of Yugoslavia to be a crime against humanity. Having discussed the morality of bombing with a British bomber pilot he describes a bombing mission from a pilot's point of view. He listens to the anguish of participants on the ground and tells the stories from both sides. He comments on the media presentation of contemporary warfare and has things to say about issues of terrorism, war, and peace

An introductory essay, probably unfair to the Serb position, explores the causes, development and consequences of the violence in Serbia and Kosovo.

"Just because I was not in the front line does not mean that I should be indifferent to crimes committed in my name. Every thinking person should know about what happened in Kosovo and the rest of Serbia in 98 and 99, and look beyond what we have been told in the media. Thinking people in Europe and America have been seriously misled about the civil war in Kosovo and the NATO bombing."

More information on www.warpoetry.co.uk

60 pages   ISBN 0 952 8969 2 3   £4-99 (UK)

Des Marshall

Des Marshall was born in Bury St Edmunds in Suffolk in 1941, the son of a Russian Jew and a Welsh coalminer's daughter who was an evacuee from London and the Blitz. He suffered so badly from asthma that he was immediately put into the Goldie Leigh Children's Hospital and Convalescent Home in Abbey Wood, London. He lived there for the first ten years of his life apart from occasional very short periods at home. As a result he has always felt that he was not wanted by his mother.

Growing up in London he found it difficult to cope with inner city life. He rejected the violence and criminality of his surroundings and worked in a wide variety of occupations including time as a stand-up comedian in holiday camps and later in London fringe clubs.

He visited Russia in the seventies and eighties and went to India to study mysticism. He had to return after three months because dysentery had brought him close to death. He has studied psychology with Dr Peter Chadwick who twice made Des a subject of his studies. (*Schizophrenia, The Positive Perspective*, and *Personality as Art*.) He became a Quaker in 1994.

His social concerns have led him to work as a volunteer in a hospice, a drop-in centre for the unemployed, mental health support organisations, a community centre, and hospitals.